Numeracy Focus

C000149438

Problem of the Week 4

Written by John Spooner

Edited by Mike Askew and Sheila Ebbutt

RIGBY

Rigby
Halley Court, Jordan Hill, Oxford, OX2 8EJ
a division of Reed Educational and Professional Publishing Ltd

Rigby is a registered trademark of Reed Educational and
Professional Publishing Ltd

OXFORD   MELBOURNE   AUCKLAND
JOHANNESBURG   BLANTYRE   GABORONE
IBADAN   PORTSMOUTH (NH)   CHICAGO

© Rigby 1999

Written by John Spooner
Edited by Mike Askew and Sheila Ebbutt

First published 1999

04 03 02 01 00 99
10 9 8 7 6 5 4 3 2 1

ISBN 0 435 21679 1

Design and page layout by Gecko Limited, Bicester, Oxon
Illustrated by Julie Anderson and Harvey Collins
Printed and bound by Ashford Press, Gosport, Hants

Contents

Introduction

Problem of the Week is an additional **Numeracy Focus** resource providing more extended investigative activities. Presented as interesting puzzles and problems, they have been designed to stimulate children's mathematical imaginations.

There is one problem for every **Numeracy Focus** teaching unit. The activities can be used for both homework and class work, and are structured for on-going use over the course of a week.

Each problem provides an investigative activity appropriate to the level of work being covered by the *Teaching and Learning File* that week.

The problems have the same format: the problem is introduced to the whole class, then children develop and solve it independently, then discuss their findings as a whole class.

Using and applying mathematics

The teaching approach taken in **Numeracy Focus** is to ensure that children use and apply the mathematics they learn in the dedicated daily maths lessons. There is scope, however, for children to work on larger-scale problems than a 45–60 minute lesson allows. *Problem of the Week* gives children the opportunity to engage in such larger-scale problems. Once they are introduced to the problem and understand it, they work independently on ways of solving it. Children are often given the opportunity to develop their own variations of the problems.

The problems have been written to ensure a balance between pure mathematical problems and problems that are set in a 'realistic' context. For example, Problem 1 is about place value and addition, but it is presented as a puzzle being debated by two friends. Problem 34 is a practical problem involved with shopping for a birthday party. The activities present problems in an imaginative context designed to interest the children.

Organization of *Problem of the Week*

Each problem is presented on a double-page spread. On the left-hand side is the teacher's page, containing instructions on how you introduce and manage the problem. On the right-hand side is a photocopiable children's page; this can be used in a number of ways, depending on the specific problem being tackled.

The teacher's and children's pages – in detail

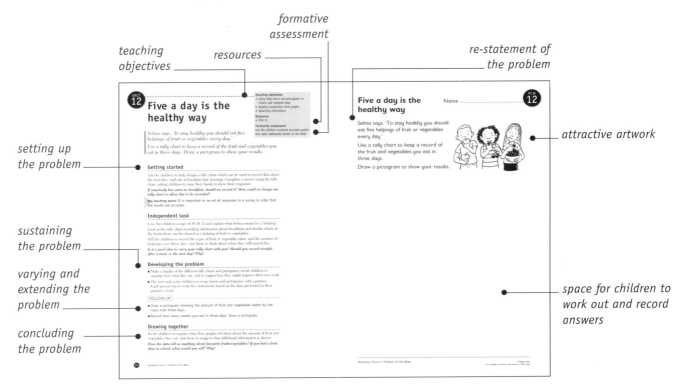

formative assessment

teaching objectives

resources

re-statement of the problem

setting up the problem

sustaining the problem

varying and extending the problem

concluding the problem

attractive artwork

space for children to work out and record answers

The teacher's page

Teaching objectives
There are three for each problem, one giving the mathematical content, and the other two emphasizing using and applying mathematics.

Resources
These are normally minimal because children are expected to do some of the work at home, and they may not have access to extra equipment. When work on the problem takes place in the classroom, standard classroom equipment is indicated.

Where equipment is suggested, you may need to offer alternatives. For example, some activities require the children to have counters. You could substitute real or plastic coins or cubes, depending on the type of activity.

Formative assessment
A question is given to help you assess a particular aspect of children's mathematical performance as they investigate the problem.

Getting started – Setting up the problem
All the problems need to be introduced to the children. You will need to allocate 10–15 minutes to explain the problem to the children and to discuss with them how to start work on it.

The teacher's page gives a starting activity for the children to do, such as a simpler, related activity, or a different example. This initial activity can be organized as class discussion, paired work or individual thinking. Suggestions are also made for giving children ideas about how to start work on the problem. You need to interest the children in the problem, and make sure that they have strategies for working on it on their own.

Independent task – Homework or in class

When you are setting up the problem, make sure you do not give solutions or best methods to the children. Rather, you should aim to set the children off in the right direction and then let them solve the problem in their own way. You need to be absolutely clear about what children should tackle independently, in what way, and how much they should do. At the same time, be careful not to overload them with too much information. One way in which the independent element has been structured is for children to do an activity on their own in preparation for working on something in the classroom. For example, they might collect data in a tally chart and then use this later in class. With these problems, you should specify what the children record on their own, if anything, and how, and make it clear what they need to bring back for discussion and continuation of the investigation.

Sustaining the problem – Developing the problem

This part of the problem is for discussing the children's progress thus far. The discussion should centre on the work the children have already done. You will need to discuss with the children the different methods they are using, and examine interim solutions they have come to.

On the teacher's page there are some questions to prompt further thinking by the children, and to encourage them to reflect on what they've done. There are also hints about what to look out for, and help for those who might be stuck.

Follow-up – Varying and extending the problem

These are ideas for children who have finished the initial problem.

Drawing together – Concluding the problem

It is important to draw the whole problem together and reach a conclusion. This gives an opportunity for discussing the final results as well as explaining and justifying different methods. This also provides the opportunity for children to present their work. You could make a final presentation of the work in the classroom, such as pinning the work on a wall, making a more formal display, or making a class book. You may choose not to have any formal recording of the problem, preferring simply to discuss the children's findings and methods. Or, you could do a presentation for assembly, if appropriate.

The photocopiable page

The photocopiable page mainly serves to remind children of the problem they are trying to solve. It can also offer useful information, a way of recording children's findings, a stimulus to further ideas, or a game to play. For some problems it may be sufficient to pin up one copy in the classroom. With other problems it would be useful for children to take the page home.

Using *Problem of the Week*

As homework

Homework should be an effective and enjoyable way of developing children's numeracy skills. **Numeracy Focus** provides three forms of homework, all of which complement each other. The *Homework* book provides short puzzles, games and problems. The *Teaching and Learning File* gives one open-ended, short activity relevant to the work in that teaching unit. The *Problem of the Week* is intended to provide an interesting challenge for children to take home at the weekend, or one night during the week.

As class work

The *Problem of the Week* can also be used to provide activities in the classroom. The children can work on the problem during the main teaching activity component of the two flexible daily maths lessons in the week.

Where *Problem of the Week* fits into Numeracy Focus planning

Problem of the Week reflects the content of **Numeracy Focus**. The problems allow children to use and apply the skills they have been learning. This gives you the flexibility to introduce *Problem of the Week* when it suits you. For example, you could use *Problem of the Week* as weekend homework or set it up during the week.

- If you choose to use *Problem of the Week* as a weekend homework, you could introduce the problem at the end of the week, on Friday. You could then discuss the children's work after the main teaching of a new topic on the following Monday.

- You may choose to set up *Problem of the Week* during the week and work on it in class. Or set it as homework early in the week and go over it at the end of the week.

Balloons

Nicky and Steve are adding up the numbers on their balloons. Steve says it is possible to make more than 20 totals that are bigger than 5000 by using sets of just three balloons. Is he right?

Teaching objectives
◆ understanding place value to 10 000
◆ reading and writing numbers to 10 000
◆ adding 1, 10, 100 and 1000 to whole numbers

Resources
◆ PCM 1
◆ counters (for Follow-up)

Formative assessment
Can the children understand place value of numbers between 5000 and 10 000?

Getting started

Give the children a copy of PCM 1 and ask them to work out what numbers can be made using just the 100 balloon and one other.

Key teaching point: A better understanding of place value can be developed by using the word 'and' between the digits when saying a number. For example, *1100 = one thousand **and** one hundred, 4325 = four thousand **and** three hundred **and** twenty **and** five.*

Independent task

Tell the children to investigate whether Steve is right. Ask them to keep a record showing how they made each of their numbers over 5000.

Developing the problem

● Invite the children to explain what they have discovered so far. Discuss which forms of recording most clearly show how the numbers were made.

● Show the children how they can keep two of the numbers constant to do a systematic search for all of the possible totals. For example:

4000 + 1000 + 1
4000 + 1000 + 2, ...

How many different totals could be made using the 4000, 1000 and one other balloon?

● Tell the children that their next task is to find how many numbers bigger than 9990 can be made using all of the balloons.

FOLLOW-UP

● Nicky says that it's possible to make every number between 1 and 11 110 using these balloons. Is she right?

● Play a game in pairs using the picture of the balloons on PCM 1. One person places a counter on five different balloons and challenges their partner to work out the total using mental addition. Each correct answer scores 1010 points.

Drawing together

Ask children to demonstrate how certain totals can be made using the numbers on the balloons. Invite children to explain their answers to the different parts of the task and discuss ways of making sure that the full range of totals is found.

Do you need to find every single number in the range to prove that it is possible to make them all?

Balloons

Nicky and Steve are adding up the numbers on the balloons below.

Steve says it is possible to make more than 20 totals that are bigger than 5000 by using sets of just three balloons.

Is he right?

Set out your work clearly.

The numbers on my balloons add up to 3420.

Lucky number

Patrick chooses six numbers between 1 and 49 when he plays the lottery. His numbers always add up to 66, his lucky number. Find ten different ways to make a total of 66 using 6 numbers.

Teaching objectives
- consolidating addition and subtraction facts to 20
- checking by using different methods
- consolidating mental strategies

Resources
- PCM 2

Formative assessment
Can the children develop strategies for adding strings of numbers?

Getting started

Give the children a copy of PCM 2 and ask them to find sets of three numbers that add up to 20. Explain that they cannot use the same number twice in the same set, for example, $10 + 5 + 5$ is not allowed. Show the children how 20 can be partitioned to make different sets, for example, $15 + 3 + 2$, $17 + 2 + 1$, ….

Key teaching point: A good understanding of addition and subtraction facts to 20 provides the foundation for further development of mental arithmetic skills. Children must learn these facts.

Independent task

Tell the children to find ten ways for Patrick to choose his numbers, keeping a clear record of the methods used in each solution. Explain that they should check each solution using a different method in order to avoid errors. Ask them to write a few sentences explaining their methods for checking.

Developing the problem

- Make a display of the different solutions discovered by the children. Discuss methods used for checking answers. Ask the children to decide whether solutions are different if they have the same numbers but in a different order.

  Will we get a different answer if we add up these numbers in a different order?

- Show the children how to add up a string of numbers by adding the most significant numbers first, and by looking for complements of 10. For example, $40 + 6 + 3 + 4 + 10 + 2$ could be added as $40 + 10 + 6 + 4 + 3 + 2$.

- Their next challenge is to find all of the possible solutions.

FOLLOW-UP

- Find sets of six numbers that add up to your own favourite number.
- Jake's lucky number is 33. Can he make only half as many combinations as Patrick can for 66?

Drawing together

Invite children to explain what they have discovered. Continue the discussion of different ways of checking for errors. Show the children how to check answers by mentally subtracting their sets of numbers from 66. Correct sets of answers produce zero, for example:

$66 - 30 \,(36) - 20 \,(16) - 10 \,(6) - 3 \,(3) - 2 \,(1) - 1 = 0$. ***That set of numbers is correct.***

$66 - 30 \,(36) - 20 \,(16) - 6 \,(10) - 5 \,(5) - 2 \,(3) - 1 = 2$. ***That set must be incorrect.***

Remind the children that addition and subtraction are inverse operations.

Lucky number

Patrick chooses six numbers between 1 and 49 when he plays the lottery.

His numbers always add up to 66, his lucky number.

Find ten different ways to make a total of 66 using 6 numbers.

Set out your work clearly.

That's 15, 20, 3, 2 and 17. I still have one more number. What should it be?

Targets

Use the digits on the dice to try to make each target number.

Getting started

Roll a dice four times to produce four single digits. Display the digits. Tell the children to investigate ways of making different numbers using addition, subtraction and these four digits. For example, *1, 2, 4* and *6* could be used to make *40 (26 + 14), 52 (64 – 12), 10 (16 – 4 – 2)*, ...

Key teaching point: The position of a digit denotes the value of that digit.

Independent task

Give the children a copy of PCM 3. Read through the rules of the activity and explain how the scoring system works. Write an example on the board:

Target 56
Solution 60. This scores 100 points as 60 is 4 more than the target (within 10).
Solution 20. This scores 50 points as 20 is 36 less than the target (within 50).

The teacher should then roll a dice six times to produce six digits. The children record these on the PCM. Tell the children to record the methods used to produce each of their solutions as they work through the task.

Developing the problem

- Invite children to report on how they have progressed with the problem. Display some of the solutions and work through the methods used to add and subtract.

  If you're working out 234 + 256, is it easier to add up the hundreds, tens or units first?

- Display examples of solutions that are not close to the target and invite children to suggest modifications. For example, *target 130, solution 12 + 23 + 36 = 71* could be modified to *21 + 32 + 63 = 116*, ...

  Point out that recording solutions that do not make an answer close to the target can be used to help you get closer, and that this approach is called trial and improvement.

- Their next task is to work with a partner and roll dice to produce their own set of six digits. They use these on another copy of PCM 3 to produce the same target numbers.

| FOLLOW-UP |

- Repeat the activity using your own sets of digits and targets.
- Play a game of 'Target challenge' with a partner. Set yourselves a target and six digits. Each person has two minutes to find a solution. The one closest to the target at the end of two minutes has 40 points. The first one to 120 points is the winner.

Drawing together

Invite children to explain how they tackled some of the targets. Look at the different methods used for recording solutions and point out any that give a clear picture of how solutions were modified to produce a closer answer. Ask children to explain what they were doing in each stage of a process of modification.

Targets

You need: a dice

Roll a dice six times.

Write the numbers in this grid.

Use all these digits to make each target number by addition and subtraction.

Try different solutions and keep a record of them. Don't use the same digit more than once in the same solution.

Use your best solution to each target to calculate your score.

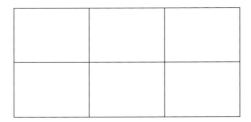

Target numbers

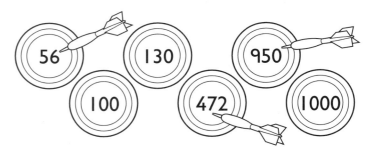

Scoring

Score 1000 points if you make a target exactly.

Score 100 points if you get within 10 of the target.

Score 50 points if you get within 50 of the target.

Target	Solutions	Score

Spaghetti machines

Teaching objectives
◆ understanding relationships between units of length
◆ breaking down a problem
◆ working back from an answer

Resources
◆ PCM 4

Formative assessment
Can the children apply their understanding of the relationship between different units of measurement to solve problems?

Each machine makes a length of spaghetti every time the handle is turned. Work out how the machines were used to make the exact amounts of spaghetti shown.

Getting started

Give the children a copy of PCM 4. Make sure that they understand that they have to add the lengths of spaghetti from the machines together to produce the various totals:

If you turn the handle of the millimetre machine once/twice, how much spaghetti is made?

How much spaghetti would you get from three turns of the metre machine?

Help the children to solve the following puzzle:

What total length of spaghetti would you get from two turns of each machine?

Key teaching point: When comparing lengths expressed in different units, it is helpful to convert each length to a common unit.

Independent task

Ask the children to work out how each length of spaghetti on PCM 4 was made. Tell them to record their solutions clearly and to check each one for errors.

Developing the problem

- Invite children to explain some of their solutions. Show examples of clear recording with a stage-by-stage approach that can easily be checked for errors.
- Show the children how to simplify the problem by using a common unit of measurement:

  The millimetre machine makes 30 mm lengths. 30 mm = 3 cm.

  The centimetre machine makes 10 cm lengths.

  To make 63 cm you could use 6 turns of 10 cm to make 60 cm and then add 3 cm.

- Their next task is to work with a partner to see how they can make double the lengths shown on the PCM.

FOLLOW-UP

- Imagine that the length of spaghetti made by each machine was halved. What would happen to the number of turns needed to make each amount?
- How many turns of the millimetre machine would be needed to make the same amount of spaghetti as five turns of the metre machine?

Drawing together

Go through some of the solutions to the problems. Use three children to model the different machines. Explain how to use common units to make it easier to solve the problems. Turn the metre lengths into centimetres to add them, and then turn the millimetres into centimetres.

Spaghetti machines

Name -------------------------------------

Each machine makes a length of spaghetti every time the handle is turned.

Work out how the machines were used to make the exact amounts of spaghetti shown below.

Record your work clearly.

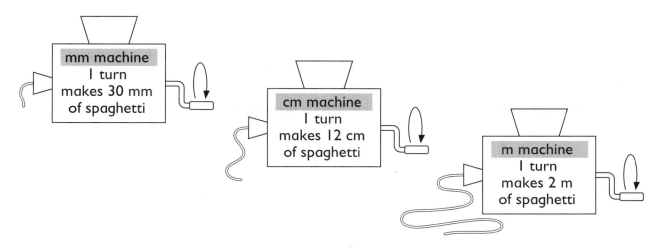

180 mm of spaghetti

_____

_____

63 cm of spaghetti

_____

_____

150 cm of spaghetti

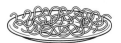

_____

_____

5 metres of spaghetti

_____

_____

9 metres of spaghetti

_____

_____

1 km of spaghetti

_____

_____

The kite shop

Teaching objectives
◆ identifying polygons
◆ visualizing 2D shape
◆ applying a range of skills

Resources
◆ PCM 5
◆ plain paper and paper-clips
◆ squared paper
◆ rulers
◆ newspaper, thin garden canes and glue
  (for Follow-up)

Formative assessment
Can the children visualize 2D shapes?

▌ *Use the shapes to design a range of kites.*

Getting started

Give the children a copy of PCM 5. Show them how to use the triangles on the PCM as a guideline to help them draw shapes. Tell them to use the PCM to draw triangles and quadrilaterals.

Key teaching point: Reflective symmetry can be used to transform triangles into quadrilaterals.

Independent task

Tell the children to use the PCM to help them design a series of kites. Look at the shapes of the kites drawn on the PCM and explain that the kites will need to be symmetrical in order to keep them balanced when they fly. Explain that they need to record their kites accurately and neatly, showing the triangles used in their designs.

Developing the problem

● Make a display of the kite designs. Look at the way in which reflections of triangles have been used to create the kite shape, and how symmetry can be used to produce a kite that is balanced. Show examples of kites made from more than two of the triangles, and look again at the link between symmetry and balance.

● Show the children how the triangles on the PCM are drawn with the help of the intersections on the squared paper. The next challenge is for children to work in pairs and use squared paper to draw a plan of one of their designs which is twice as big as the original.

┌─────────────┐
│ FOLLOW-UP │
└─────────────┘

● Make a display of shapes made from the triangles which are not kites. Find names for as many as you can.

● Make a real kite out of newspaper using an enlarged version of your plan as a template. Glue thin garden canes around the perimeter and across the diagonals of the kite. Make a tail out of small triangles.

Drawing together

Show the children some of the finished kite shapes and ask them to guess which shapes from the PCM were used. Ask children to give examples of maths used when planning and building their kites.

How could you work out the lengths of the triangles needed if you enlarged this plan?

What will happen if this side is heavier than the other? How could we test the kite in the classroom to see if it is balanced?

Find a safe place to fly the kites.

The kite shop

Name ------------------------------------

You need: paper, paper-clips

Use the shapes below to design a range of kites.

Put paper over the shapes and trace them.

Record your kite designs.

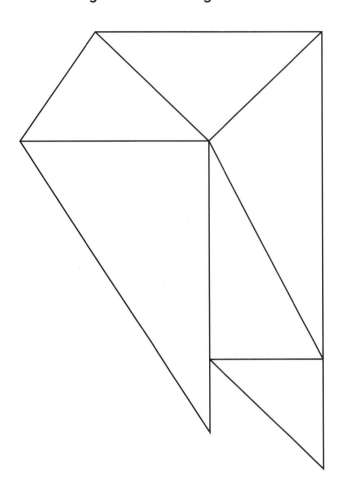

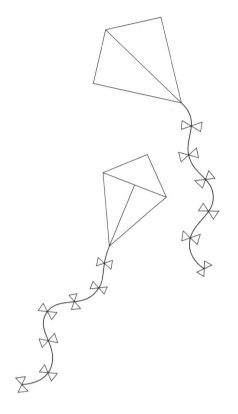

The frog obstacle race

Teaching objectives
◆ working back from an answer
◆ checking results
◆ explaining reasoning

Resources
PCM 6

Formative assessment
Can the children use inverse operations to work back from an answer?

Double the number on the frog when it jumps over a hurdle.
Subtract from the number when the frog crawls through a mud tunnel.
Work out the number on the frog at the start of each race.

Getting started

Give the children a copy of PCM 6 and explain what happens to the number on the frog as it goes through the obstacles in the race. Tell the children to work out what number will be on frog 11 at the end of the race.

Key teaching point: Keeping a step-by-step record of the changes in the number helps with checking results.

Independent task

Tell the children to find the number on each frog at the start, keeping a step-by-step record showing how they found each solution.

Developing the problem

● Invite children to explain how they found the missing numbers on the frogs.

● Show the children how to use inverse operations to find the starting number:

We can work back from the 79 frog by doing the opposite of what happened in the race $79 + 1 = 80 \div 2 = 40 \div 2 = 20 + 1 = 21$. So the 79 frog must have started with the number 21.

Check by going from the start of the race:

$21 - 1 = 20 \times 2 = 40 \times 2 = 80 - 1 = 79$.

● Their next task is to draw a frog obstacle race in which the finished frog is numbered 100. They should then ask a partner to find the starting number.

FOLLOW-UP

● Draw four different obstacle races in which the finished frog is numbered 105.

● Invent frog puzzles for a partner using different types of obstacle.

Drawing together

Draw a frog obstacle race, put in a finishing number and ask the children to calculate the starting number.

Show the children how to use inverse operations to work back from the answer:

Then check the answer by working from the start:

Invite children to make up and draw other obstacle races for the class to solve.

The frog obstacle race

Name ------------------------------------

Double the number on the frog when it jumps over a hurdle.

Subtract 1 from the number when the frog crawls through a mud tunnel.

Work out the number on the frog at the start of each race.

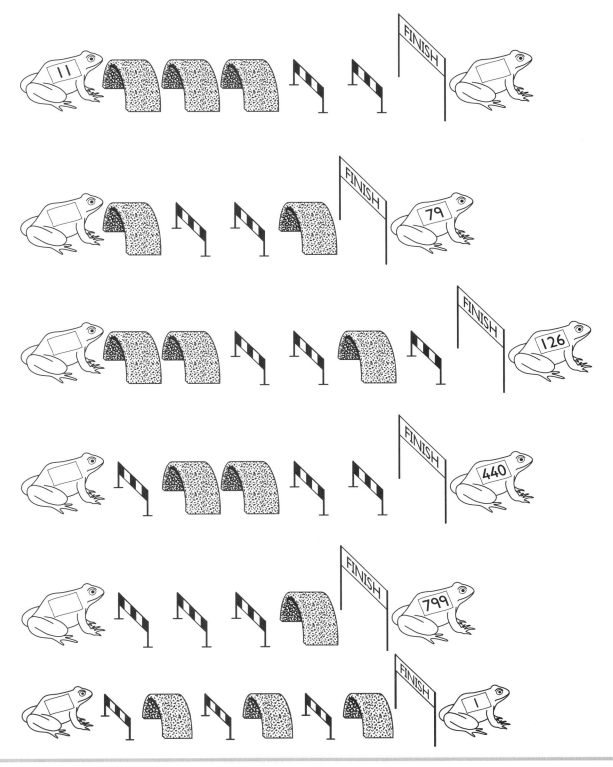

The Numberline Express

Teaching objectives
- extending number sequences beyond zero
- developing systems to generate results
- breaking down a problem

Resources
- PCM 7
- small counters (one each)
- paper

Formative assessment
Can the children test statements and produce evidence to justify findings?

The train starts at Noughton. In the morning it goes through Twentyover. In the afternoon it goes through Twentyunder.
On Monday it stops at every second station along the line.
On Tuesday it stops at every third station along the line.
On Wednesday it stops at every fourth station.
On Thursday it stops at every fifth station.
On Friday it stops at every sixth station. The train does not run on Saturdays or Sundays.

Decide whether the statements are always true, sometimes true or never true.

Getting started

Give the children a copy of PCM 7 and a counter. Explain that the counter can be used as the train. Tell the children to place the counter on Noughton and work out at which stations it stops on Monday morning and Monday afternoon.

Key teaching point: The number system continues back beyond zero.

Independent task

Ask the children to investigate the statements on PCM 7. Ask them to decide whether each is sometimes true, never true or always true. Ask the children to produce evidence on paper to support their decisions.

Developing the problem

- Display a large table with three columns labelled 'Sometimes true', 'Always true' and 'Never true'. Ask different children to come up and write out one of the statements under the heading they think most appropriate. Invite children to show examples of any charts or drawings they used to solve this problem. Show the children how to use a table to help solve the problem.

- Their next task is to work in pairs to make up another statement for each column.

FOLLOW-UP

- Which of the statements would still be true if the train ran on Saturdays stopping at every seventh station, and ran on Sundays, stopping at every eighth?

- Draw up a timetable for the Numberline Express showing where it stops each day.

Drawing together

Look at the display of statements and invite children to show how they decided where to place them. Model the problem by getting children to stand in a line. Give the child at each end and the one in the middle, a piece of paper. These represent the three stations. Invite children to play the part of the train, stopping at the correct stations on Monday, Tuesday, …

The Numberline Express

Name --

You need: a counter and some paper

The train starts at Noughton. In the morning it
goes through Twentyover. In the afternoon it
goes through Twentyunder.
On Monday it stops at every second station along
the line.
On Tuesday it stops at every third station along
the line.
On Wednesday it stops at every fourth station.
On Thursday it stops at every fifth station.
On Friday it stops at every sixth station.
The train does not run on Saturdays or Sundays.

Decide whether these statements are always true,
sometimes true or never true.

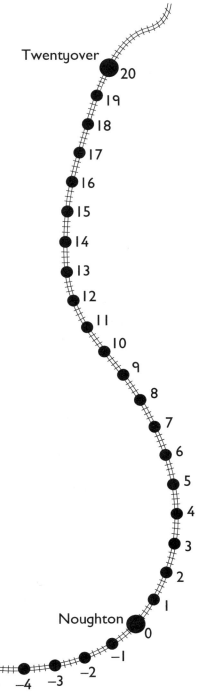

Statements	Always, sometimes or never true?
The train stops at every station.	
The train stops at 8 in the mornings.	
The train goes past more stations than it stops at.	
The train stops at −11.	
The train stops at 12.	
The train stops at −9 in the afternoons.	
The train stops at Twentyunder.	

Spending spree

Teaching objectives
- consolidating rapid recall of multiplication facts
- using inverse operations
- looking for a range of solutions

Resources
- PCM 8
- dice
- paper

Formative assessment
Can the children use inverse operations to work back from an answer to find a range of solutions?

▌ *Play the game and solve the puzzles.*

Getting started

The children should work with a partner. Give them a copy of PCM 8 and a dice. Explain that the 6 will count as 10 in the game that they are about to play.

They may find it easier to cover the 6 with a sticker or piece of tape marked 10.

Explain the rules and allow the children to play.

▶ **Key teaching point:** Multiplication facts are linked to division facts. For example, $3 \times 5 = 15$ so $15 \div 5 = 3$.

Independent task

Point out the puzzles on the PCM and ask the children to predict the number of solutions there could be for each puzzle. Record these predictions for later discussion. Tell the children to play the game to investigate the puzzles, and to record each of the solutions they discover on paper.

Developing the problem

- Compare children's predictions about the number of solutions to each puzzle with the number of solutions they actually discovered. Ask the children to explain the methods they used to find each solution.

- Show the children how inverse operations could be used to discover a solution, for example, *How could you get 32p if the dice throw was 4?* $\square \times 4 = 32$; $32 \div 4 = 8$.

- Show the children how trial and improvement can be used, for example, *How could you get 42p if the dice was throw was 3? 15p × 3 = 45p (too big). 13p × 3 = 39p (too small). 14p × 3 = 42p.*

- Their next challenge is to work with a partner to find all of the possible amounts that can be made by one throw of a dice which always lands showing 5.

| FOLLOW-UP |

- Find the largest and smallest amount of money that can be spent after six rolls of the dice.

- Set a puzzle for a friend to solve.

Drawing together

Ask the children to use PCM 8 to help them solve a range of problems, for example,

How could I spend 40p or 16p or 56p with just one roll? If I landed on a 12p chocolate, what totals can I make? What's the least/most I can spend after one roll? ...

Spending spree

PCM
8

You need: paper, a dice

Play the game and solve the puzzles.

Rules

Roll a dice onto the picture below.

Multiply the number on the dice by the price of the chocolate bar it lands on. The answer tells you how much money you have spent. Record it on paper. See who spends the most in 10 goes.

Puzzles

I got 32p. Guess how I did it.

I got 97p after a few goes. Can you see how?

I can get 60p with one roll in five different ways. Can you?

How many ways can you make £1 with just two rolls?

Threes rule

Casey has made up a 3 times table rule. She says, 'If the digits of a number add up to 3, 6 or 9, the number is in the 3 times table.' Emika says that Casey's rule doesn't always work. Who is right?

Teaching objectives
- developing written methods for multiplication and division
- looking for patterns
- making and testing statements

Resources
- PCM 9
- calculators

Formative assessment
Can the children produce evidence to test and support statements?

Getting started

Give the children a copy of PCM 9 and look at Casey's rule. Explain what Casey means by showing the children how the digits of 12 (1 + 2 = 3), 15 (1 + 5 = 6) and 18 (1 + 8 = 9) can be added to make 3, 6 or 9. Show the children how to test whether these numbers are multiples of 3 using multiplication and division. Ask them to see which other numbers on the PCM are multiples of 3.

Key teaching point: Inverse operations can be used to check answers.

Independent task

Tell the children to investigate Casey's rule. Ask them to make lists of numbers that obey the rule. Tell them to record how they tested whether a number was a multiple of 3, and to look for examples of numbers that break Casey's rule.

Developing the problem

- Make a display of numbers that obey Casey's rule and ask the children to add examples. Ask them to explain how they tested numbers to see if they were multiples of 3. Give the children calculators and show them how to use division to check the numbers.

- Make another collection of numbers: multiples of 3 with digits that don't add up to 3, 6 or 9. Ask the children to see if they can spot a pattern in the numbers in this group (their digits add up to multiples of 3, 6 or 9).
  Are 99, 189, 198, 279 and 396 multiples of 3? What happens if you add up the digits? What about 1008 or 2007?

- Their next task is to work with a partner using a calculator to investigate multiples of 3 to find a pattern and use it to make up their own threes rule.

FOLLOW-UP

- Make a list of all of the patterns you can see in the 3 times table.

- See if you can discover a sixes rule for the 6 times table.

Drawing together

Make a display of threes rules made by the children, along with a statement about each pattern used to make the rule. Discuss which rules most accurately describe the patterns found in the 3 times table.

Play a game of 'Odd one out'. The teacher gives each of three children a number on a piece of paper (one or two of which should be multiples of 3). The children hold up the numbers, and the rest of the class have to spot the odd one out.

Threes rule

Casey has made up a 3 times table rule.

She says, 'If the digits of a number add up to 3, 6 or 9, the number is in the 3 times table.'

Emika says that Casey's rule doesn't always work.

Who is right?

Set out your work clearly.

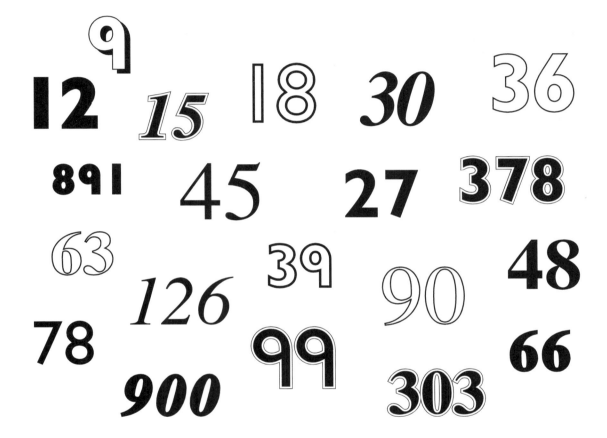

9

12   15   18   30   36

891   45   27   378

63   39   48

126   90

78   99   66

900   303

The Fractious family

Teaching objectives
◆ finding fractions of numbers and
  quantities
◆ breaking down problems
◆ selecting maths to use

Resources
◆ PCM 10

Formative assessment
Can the children apply their understanding
of fractions?

The children in the Fractious family always argue when it comes to sharing. Mum set out a new rule: Peggy gets $\frac{1}{2}$ of the total. Annie gets $\frac{1}{4}$ of the total. Ben and Jamie each get $\frac{1}{2}$ of what's left.

Show how the family would share these items.

Getting started

Organize the children in groups of three and ask them to work out how they would share each of the following items: *12 sweets, a circular pizza, 4 apples, 8 cakes, £2.91 and 1 litre of orange squash.*

Key teaching point: Fractions are related to division.

Independent task

Give the children a copy of PCM 10 and explain the activity. Tell the children to record their solutions using calculations or drawings where appropriate.

Developing the problem

● Invite children to explain their solutions and show methods of recording. Look at examples that are difficult to share accurately in real life.

   How would you share the litre of ice-cream? Would it be possible to measure out those amounts of ice-cream as accurately as the rule says? Can you give fair shares in real life without being absolutely accurate?

● Show the children how to draw out a box made up of 8 equal parts. Colour $\frac{4}{8}$, $\frac{2}{8}$ and two separate $\frac{1}{8}$s and relate the sizes of the boxes to the shares needed by the Fractious family. Show the children how this can be used to help solve the problem.

● Their next task is to work with a partner and suggest other things that the family might share.

FOLLOW-UP

● Work out how a family of three children could divide the amounts on the PCM if they shared things $\frac{1}{2}$, $\frac{1}{3}$, $\frac{1}{6}$.

● Work out a rule for sharing things fairly in your class.

Drawing together

Display the finished work and ask children to explain how certain quantities can be shared.

How would you share out 1 kg of peanuts? Would you count the nuts or weigh them? How can you share out liquids accurately? How can a circular pizza be cut into fair shares?

The Fractious family

Name ----------------------------------

The children in the Fractious family
always argue when it comes to sharing.
Mum set out a new rule:

Peggy gets $\frac{1}{2}$ of the total.

Annie gets $\frac{1}{4}$ of the total.

Ben and Jamie each get $\frac{1}{2}$ of what's left.

Show how the family would share the following items.

Set out your work clearly.

UNIT 11

A longer working week

Teaching objectives
- using calendars
- organizing data in tables
- solving puzzles

Resources
- PCM 11
- calendars
- paper

Formative assessment
Can the children use calendars to answer questions?

A special new working week is planned for school children. Each week lasts 10 days. 8 of these days are spent at school. There will be no change to the number of days in each month. January 1st will be a Monday.

Draw a calendar showing the days, weeks and months of the new school year.

Getting started

Give the children a copy of PCM 11 and a calendar showing the current year. Help them to fill in the calendar page for January. Ask them to compare this new style January with the present one.

How many more school days will there be? How many weekend days will you have? Will school Saturdays ever fall on the same day as normal Saturdays? …

Key teaching point: Calendars organize data in table form.

Independent task

Tell the children to complete the calendar for the year on a separate sheet of paper. Suggest that they record the months in the way shown on the PCM for January.

Look at a copy of a calendar with the children. Draw their attention to the last and first days of each month. Point out that the first day of each month is not always a Monday.

Developing the problem

- Invite children to explain what they have found. Check that the children have the correct number of days in each month.
- Ask the children to suggest some investigations using the new calendar, for example:

  What day will your birthday be? Where should end-of-term holidays be?
  How many days will we have to come to school each year?
  Will swimming still be every Wednesday or on days that used to be Wednesdays?

- Their next challenge is to investigate some of the questions they have thought up.

FOLLOW-UP

- Write a letter explaining your opinions about the new school week. Is it a good idea? Will it help children to learn more? Is it fair?
- Draw a calendar based on a week with the days Monday, Tuesday, Wednesday, Saturday1, Saturday2, Sunday1, Sunday2.

Drawing together

Ask children for their opinions about a change to the length of the school week. Ask a series of questions based on the existing calendar, for example:

How many days have we been at school this month? What will be the date on this day next week? How many days are there in this/next month?

A longer working week

Name ---------------------------------------

You need: a calendar, paper

A special new working week is planned for school children.

Each week lasts 10 days.

8 of these days are spent at school.

There will be no change to the number of days in each month.

January 1st will be a Monday.

Draw a calendar showing the days, weeks and months of the new school year.

Five a day is the healthy way

Teaching objectives
◆ using tally charts and pictograms to collect and interpret data
◆ drawing conclusions from graphs
◆ obtaining information

Resources
◆ PCM 12

Formative assessment
Can the children construct accurate graphs and make statements based on the data?

Selma says, 'To stay healthy you should eat five helpings of fruit or vegetables every day.'

Use a tally chart to keep a record of the fruit and vegetables you eat in three days. Draw a pictogram to show your results.

Getting started

Ask the children to help design a tally chart which can be used to record data about the food they each ate at breakfast that morning. Complete a survey using the tally chart, asking children to raise their hands to show their responses.

If somebody has eaten no breakfast, should we record it? How could we design our tally chart to allow this to be recorded?

Key teaching point: It is important to record all responses in a survey in order that the results are accurate.

Independent task

Give the children a copy of PCM 12 and explain what Selma means by a 'helping'.

Look at the tally chart recording information about breakfasts and decide which of the foods there can be classed as a helping of fruit or vegetables.

Tell the children to record the types of fruit or vegetable eaten, and the number of helpings, over three days. Ask them to think about when they will record this:

Is it a good idea to carry your tally chart with you? Should you record straight after a meal, or the next day? Why?

Developing the problem

● Make a display of the different tally charts and pictograms. Invite children to consider how clear they are, and to suggest how they might improve their own work.

● The next task is for children to swap charts and pictograms with a partner. Each person has to write five statements based on the data presented in their partner's work.

FOLLOW-UP

● Draw a pictogram showing the amount of fruit and vegetables eaten by the class over three days.

● Record how many sweets you eat in three days. Draw a pictogram.

Drawing together

Invite children to explain what their graphs tell them about the amount of fruit and vegetables they eat. Ask them to suggest what additional information is shown:

Does the data tell us anything about favourite fruits/vegetables? If you had a fruit shop in school, what would you sell? Why?

Five a day is the healthy way

Name ----------------------------------

Selma says, 'To stay healthy you should eat five helpings of fruit or vegetables every day.'

Use a tally chart to keep a record of the fruit and vegetables you eat in three days.

Draw a pictogram to show your results.

Little Red Robyn Hood

Robyn shoots three arrows at the target.
Find out how she could have made her
different scores.

Teaching objectives
◆ using multiplication and division
◆ working back from an answer
◆ checking results

Resources
◆ PCM 13
◆ paper

Formative assessment
Can the children use their understanding
of multiplication and division to check
results?

Getting started

Display a copy of the target from PCM 13. Explain that an arrow scores 10 times the number it hits on the target. Tell the children to work out all the scores this arrow could make. Ask them to work out what scores could be made with two of these arrows.

▶ **Key teaching point:** Multiplying a number by 10 moves the number one space to the left on the H T Ones board.

Independent task

Give the children a copy of PCM 13 and tell them to investigate how Robyn made her scores. Tell them to record on a separate sheet of paper how they solved each problem and ask them to write a few sentences explaining 'How to check your work'.

Developing the problem

● Invite children to explain some of their solutions. Ask children to read out their 'How to check your work' tips and use these to check some solutions.

● Show the children how to break down the problem:
  3390 is a large score so we can guess that the × 100 arrow hit a large number. 34 × 100 = 3400 which is too large. 31 × 100 gives 3100 which means that the other arrows had to score 290 between them. How could that have been done?

● Their next task is to work out ten other totals that Robyn could score.

FOLLOW-UP

● Find the best ten scores Robyn could make with just two × 100 arrows.

● Make your own target and use the three arrows to make six different scores. Challenge a partner to find how the totals were made.

Drawing together

Invite children to explain their methods for checking results.

Show the children how to check their answers using division:

Let's look at the solution to 3390.
The ×100 arrow scores 3100. 3100 ÷ 100 = 31 which is on the target.
The ×10 arrow scores 80. 80 ÷ 10 = 8 which is on the target.
The ×10 arrow scores 210. 210 ÷ 10 = 21 which is on the target.
Therefore this solution is correct. There may be other solutions too.

Invite children to challenge the class to find out how they made certain scores. They tell the class the total score and the number scored by one of the arrows. The class must then guess the score of the other arrows.

Little Red Robyn Hood

Name --------------------------------------

Robyn shoots three arrows at the target.

Find out how she could have made her different scores.

Record your work clearly.

Two of the arrows multiply the number hit by 10.

One of the arrows multiplies the number hit by 100.

Robyn's scores

3390	4010
280	1080
890	940

Penny falls

Move the penny through the maze, adding on the amounts it lands on. Make 15 different totals.

Teaching objectives
◆ adding by adjusting by 1
◆ selecting methods of recording results
◆ suggesting extensions

Resources
◆ PCM 14
◆ 1p coins or counters (one per child)
◆ £1 coins or counters (for Follow-up)

Formative assessment
Can the children mentally add or subtract strings of numbers?

Getting started

Give the children a coin or counter and a copy of PCM 14. Show the children how the coin moves through the maze, adding the amounts of money that it lands on until it falls out at the bottom. Ask the children to suggest different ways of recording the route taken and the totals made.

▶ **Key teaching point:** Adding the amounts in the maze is made easier by rounding to the nearest ten and then adjusting the answer.

Independent task

Tell the children to make 15 different totals, recording how they made each one on a piece of paper.

Developing the problem

● Invite children to explain how they made some of their totals. Ask children to explain their methods for calculating and checking answers. Examine some of the methods used to record the routes.

● Show the children how to map a route using arrows and keeping a running total, for example,

$$1p \xrightarrow{+} 8p \xrightarrow{+} 19p \xrightarrow{+} 19p \xrightarrow{+} 21p$$
$$9p \qquad 28p \qquad 47p \qquad 68p, \ldots$$

● Their next task is to draw an additional layer of triangles beneath the maze on the PCM. They can choose amounts to write in the spaces. Tell them to produce a set of ten totals from their new maze.

FOLLOW-UP

● Make and play a game of 'Penny falls' using spaces marked with different numbers such as 18p, 38p, 42p, and so on. Write a list of hints on how to work out the answers in your head.

● Make a different version of the game called 'Pound falls'. Start with £1 and subtract the amounts you land on as you go through the maze.

Drawing together

Display a large copy of the 'Penny falls' maze and invite children to trace a route slowly through the maze. Ask the rest of the class to keep count of the total.

Give the children copies of the 'Penny falls' and 'Pound falls' games made by other children. Invite them to investigate the different totals that can be made.

Penny falls

Name --

You need: a coin or counter, paper

Move the penny through the maze, adding on the amounts it lands on.
Make 15 different totals.

Keep a record on a piece of paper to show how you made each total.

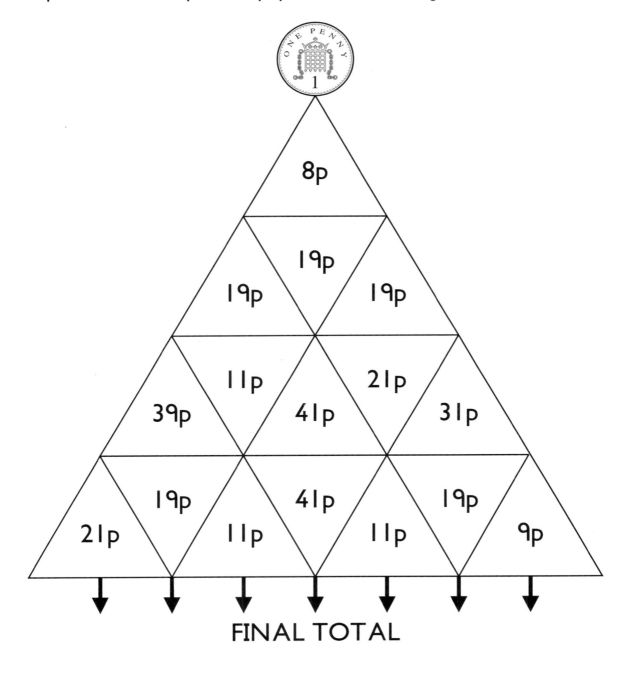

FINAL TOTAL

Playing cards

Teaching objectives
◆ using addition and subtraction
◆ breaking down a problem
◆ modelling problems

Resources
◆ PCM 15
◆ scrap paper

Formative assessment
Can the children use addition and subtraction to solve a problem?

Each person has four cards chosen from a set of odd numbers 71 to 109. Look at the clues to work out which card each person has.

Getting started

Display the odd numbers 11 to 31. Tell the children to work with a partner and make cards out of scrap paper to show each of these numbers. Tell the children that you have picked two of these cards which have a sum of *42 (15 + 27)*. Ask them to work out all of the number pairs you could have picked.

Ask the children to take it in turns to choose two of the cards. They tell their partner the sum of the cards and ask the partner to guess the two cards chosen.

Key teaching point: Modelling a problem can make it easier to solve.

Independent task

Give the children a copy of PCM 15 and explain that they have to find out which cards the people are holding. Tell them to explain in stages how they used the clues to find each set of four cards.

Developing the problem

● Ask for a volunteer to explain how they identified one of the people's cards. Write a step-by-step record of the child's approach. Draw attention to the importance of wrong answers in arriving at the correct solution.

● Show the children how making a set of the cards out of scrap paper can help in solving the problem:

If we know that this person has these four cards, then we know that these cards can't be in this other person's set. When we have worked out three of the problems, we know 12 cards that can't be in the last set. Will that make it easier to work out?

● Their next task is to write one more clue for each person's set of cards.

| FOLLOW-UP |

● In groups, play a game using one set of the odd number cards 71 to 109. Each player picks four cards and then writes down the sum of their cards. They place two cards face down and two cards face up next to their total. Players take it in turns to guess the identity of the hidden cards.

● Design your own version of the game. Select different cards and clues for each player. Give your problem to someone else to solve.

Drawing together

● Invite children to reveal the identity of the four sets of cards:

Carly 71, 73, 75, 77.   Stevie 79, 89, 99, 109.
Jamie 101, 103, 105, 107.   Holly 81, 91, 87, 97.

● Look at the step-by-step methods used by the children. Display the whole range of numbers, crossing off the sets of four to show how the search can be narrowed down.

Playing cards

Name ----------------------------------

You need: scrap paper

Each person has four cards chosen from a set of odd numbers 71 to 109.

Look at the clues to work out which cards each person has.

Record your work clearly.

My cards add up to 296.
I've got four consecutive
odd numbers.

My cards have the sum of 376.
I've got five 9 digits on my cards.

I get 416 when I add up my cards. I've got
four numbers that are greater than 100.

I get a total of 356 when I add them up. The
difference between my biggest number and
my smallest number is 16.

Baby elephant on a see-saw

Teaching objectives
◆ using grams and kilograms
◆ searching for information
◆ selecting maths

Resources
◆ PCM 16
◆ balance scales and masses
◆ tins and packages of foods
◆ paper
◆ ruler, card, pencil and small objects
  (for Follow-up)

Formative assessment
Can the children find the masses of a variety of objects and compare them with a larger mass?

The average mass of a baby elephant is 120 kg. Make a display of things that you could put on the other end of the see-saw to balance the mass of the elephant.

Getting started

Show the children the food packages and ask them to read the masses. Ask them to estimate how many of each package would balance a 1 kg mass. Use the balance and masses to test their ideas using a kilogram mass on one side and the package or sets of masses equivalent to the package on the other. For example, if a package weighs 400 g, pairs of 200 g masses could be used to represent the package.

Key teaching point: One kilogram weighs the same as 1000 grams.

Independent task

Give the children a copy of PCM 16. Tell them to find different sets of objects that could be used to balance the elephant, for example, *600 tins of baked beans.* Tell them to show their calculations and to present each idea neatly on paper so that it can be used as an illustration in a story book about the elephant.

Developing the problem

● Invite children to show examples of the sets of objects they have found and to explain how they worked out that this would balance the mass of the elephant.

● Show the children how to use repeated addition and multiplication to work out the equivalent masses. Show them how multiples of 10 or 100 of any object can be calculated quickly.

● Their next task is to work with a partner to make a story book about the elephant on the see-saw and their efforts to make it balance.

FOLLOW-UP

● Find out the mass of a giraffe or a dinosaur. Explain how you would get such an animal to balance on the see-saw.

● Make a see-saw. Put a mass on one end and find small objects to make it balance.

Drawing together

Invite children to explain what they have found. Draw their attention to examples that clearly show the calculations used to reach the answer. Show the children how to use division to check their calculations.

Baby elephant on a see-saw

Name --

The average mass of a baby elephant is 120 kg.

Make a display of things that you could put on the other end of the see-saw to balance the mass of the elephant.

Show your calculations. Record each idea neatly on paper.

The golden carrot

Golden carrots will be on sale soon. You have entered the competition to design a box for a golden carrot.

Teaching objectives
- ◆ exploring links between 2D and 3D shapes
- ◆ visualizing 3D shapes
- ◆ making accurate measurements

Resources
- ◆ PCM 17
- ◆ carrots
- ◆ card
- ◆ rulers
- ◆ squared paper
- ◆ glue
- ◆ apple and banana (for Follow-up)

Formative assessment
Can the children plan and build 3D shapes from nets?

Getting started

Give the children a copy of PCM 17 and a carrot. Explain that the carrot growers are looking for a design for a box that will help them sell their carrots. Discuss the competition rules on the PCM. Tell the children to measure the carrot and list the dimensions they think are needed for their task.

Key teaching point: The three dimensions of a 3D shape are length, width and height.

Independent task

Tell the children to design a box for a golden carrot. Tell them that their finished work should include both the box and a copy of the net used to build it.

Developing the problem

- ● Make a display of the boxes and their nets and invite children to explain how they planned and made their box.

   How did you know how wide to make the box?
   What other measurements did you make?
   How did you hold the sides of the box together?

- ● Show the children how to measure a carrot and design the box so that it is slightly larger than the carrot. Use squared paper to produce a draft version of the box. Show the children how to include flaps for gluing the sides together and how to use the draft version of the net as a template when drawing out the plan on the card.

- ● Their next task is to work with a partner to plan the net of a box that could be used to carry six of their golden carrot boxes.

FOLLOW-UP

- ● Design a box to hold a silver apple or a bronze banana.
- ● Find out how many of your boxes could be made from a single sheet of A4 card.

Drawing together

Invite a 'special guest' to judge the finished work in relation to the rules set out on PCM 17. Award golden carrots to all of the worthy entrants.

How could we stop the carrot rolling about?
How could we allow the carrot to be seen?
Is the neatness of the finished box important? How could we make this box neater?

The golden carrot

You need: a carrot, some card, a ruler, squared paper, glue

Golden carrots will be on sale soon.

You have entered the competition to design a box for a golden carrot.

The Golden Carrot Box Design Competition

✳ ✳ ✳ ✳ ✳ ✳ ✳ ✳ ✳

Win a weekend break.
Yes, two whole days off school!!

Rules

Golden carrots will be on sale for £3.00 each.

They are expensive, so they need a fancy-looking box.

A person looking at the box should be able to see the golden carrot.

Golden carrots must not roll about in their box.

Nice ice-creams

Teaching objectives
◆ developing a systematic approach
◆ checking answers
◆ looking for patterns

Resources
◆ PCM 18
◆ paper

Formative assessment
Can the children organize their work in a systematic way?

*The ice-cream van outside Vicky's school has a
new ice-cream cornet.
'Two scoops of ice-cream for 40p.
Six different flavours to choose from.'
Vicky says she can choose a different combination
of flavours every day for 20 days. Is she correct?*

Getting started

Give the children a copy of PCM 18 and explain the problem. Ask them to work out
all of the combinations that would be possible if one of the two scoops was always
vanilla. Point out that pairs such as vanilla/strawberry and strawberry/vanilla both
count as the same combination.

Ask the children to predict the number of different combinations they think will be
possible. Record any calculations used to make these predictions.

Key teaching point: Keeping one value constant helps when tackling a problem
involving variables.

Independent task

Ask the children to investigate whether Vicky is correct. Tell them to record all the
different combinations that they find on paper.

Developing the problem

● Invite children to say how many different combinations they found. Ask if they
  discovered any patterns that helped them find all the possible combinations. Show
  the children how to organize the problem by keeping one of the variables constant:

*Let's use the initials of the flavours to record our work, and keep one scoop
strawberry.
So we can have S + S, S + P, S + C, S + L, S + T, S + V.
Now let's keep one scoop peach .
So we can have P + P, P + C, P + L, P + T, P + V. We've already got P + S.*

● Their next task is to work out how many combinations would be possible if
  butterscotch was added to the list of flavours.

FOLLOW-UP

● How many different combinations would be possible if there were 10 different
  flavours to choose from?

● How many different combinations would be possible if each cornet was made
  from three scoops chosen from four different flavours?

Drawing together

Invite children to show their work. Compare their findings with the predictions made
at the start. Show the children how patterns can be used in this type of problem:

S + S, S + P, S + C, S + L, S + T, S + V = 6 combinations

P + P, P + C, P + L, P + T, P + V = 5 combinations

C + C, C + L, C + T, C + V = 4 combinations ...

Nice ice-creams

Name ----------------------------------

You need: paper

The ice-cream van outside Vicky's school has a new ice-cream cornet.

Two scoops of
ice-cream for **40p**

*Six different flavours
to choose from:*

STRAWBERRY
VANILLA
PEACH
CHOCOLATE
LEMON
TOFFEE

I can choose a
different combination
of flavours every day
for 20 days.

Is Vicky correct?

Record your work clearly.

Temperature in Zog

Teaching objectives
◆ using negative numbers in the context of temperature
◆ solving mathematical problems
◆ using diagrams and tables to solve problems

Resources
◆ PCM 19
◆ number lines –20 to 20

Formative assessment
Are the children able to use diagrams to help them find solutions?

On the first day of the month in Zog the temperature is always 0 °C. The second day is always ___ than the first. The third day is always 1 °C colder than the second. The fourth day is always 1 °C colder than the third and so on until halfway through the month. From the sixteenth onwards it warms up by 1 °C each day until the last day. There are 30 days in every Zog month. What will be the temperature in Zog on the twelfth and eighteenth day?

Getting started

Give each child a copy of PCM 19 and and talk about the pattern of temperature changes in Zog. Draw a thermometer on the board and look at the pattern of temperature change from the first day to the fourth day.

▶ **Key teaching point:** Diagrams and tables can help you to understand a problem by making the problem visible.

Independent task

The children choose five different days, including the twelfth and eighteenth, and work out the temperatures on these days. They fill in the temperatures on the blank thermometers. Tell them to record any diagrams or tables used to solve the problem.

Developing the problem

Invite children to show their work and to explain any patterns they noticed in the answers. Look at examples of tables or diagrams used to solve the problem.

● Show the children how tables can help to reveal patterns in answers:

Day	Temperature change	Temperature
1	0	0 °C
2	– 1	– 1 °C
3	– 1	– 2 °C

● Their next challenge is to work out what the temperature on different days of the month would be if the days got colder by 2 °C each day until halfway through the month, then 2 °C warmer each day.

FOLLOW-UP

● What if the temperature went down 2 °C each day for the first half of the month, then up 3 °C each day? What would the temperature be on the last day?

Drawing together

Make a display of the children's work and explain the importance of clear, organized presentation of work including tables and diagrams, as an aid to finding solutions and communicating results.

Temperature in Zog

Name ------------------------------------

You need: paper

On the first day of the month in Zog the temperature is always 0 °C.
The second day is always 1 °C colder than the first. The third day is
always 1 °C colder than the second. The fouth day is always 1 °C
colder than the third and so on until halfway through the month. From
the sixteenth onwards it warms up by 1 °C each day until the last day.
There are 30 days in every Zog month.

What will be the temperature in Zog on the twelfth and eighteenth
day?

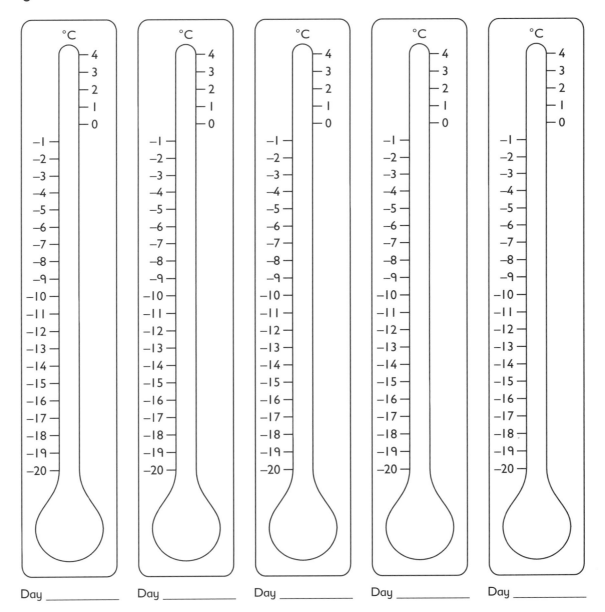

Dartboard digits

Teaching objectives
◆ developing rapid recall of multiplying 6, 7, 8 and 9
◆ searching for a range of solutions
◆ presenting results

Resources
◆ PCM 20
◆ dice and paper (for Follow-up)

Formative assessment
Can the children work back from an answer to find out how a number was produced?

Umit throws four darts at the dartboard. He always hits the target. Find 13 different scores that he could make.

Getting started

Display a large copy of the dartboard on PCM 20 and ask the children to work out which numbers between 6 and 20 they can make using just two darts.

Key teaching point: Multiplication is a form of repeated addition.

Independent task

Give the children a copy of PCM 20. Ask them to work out the largest and smallest numbers they can make using four darts. Ask them to predict whether it is possible to make all of the numbers between these numbers. Record some of these predictions.

Tell them to find 13 different scores and to record how they made each one.

Ask them to present their answers in order of size.

Developing the problem

● List in ascending order the numbers made by the children. Compare the results with the predictions made by the children.

   What numbers are missing? Is it possible to make these?

● Show the children how to organize their search for the range of answers by starting with the smallest possible answer:

   $6 \times 4 = 24$ is the smallest score he can make.
   That's the same as $6 + 6 + 6 + 6 = 24$.

   $6 \times 3 + 7$ must be the next biggest possible score, because that's the same as $6 + 6 + 6 + \boxed{6 + 1} = 25$.
   Next we try $6 \times 3 + 8$. That's $6 + 6 + 6 + \boxed{6 + 2} = 26$.

● Their next task is to find out whether all of the numbers between 6 and 36 are possible if some of the darts are allowed to miss and score 0.

FOLLOW-UP

● What scores can Umit make using six darts?

● Play 'Dartboard digits'. Make a large copy of the dartboard. Roll a dice onto the dartboard. Multiply the number on the dice by the number that the dice landed on. Play on your own by recording how many throws it takes to reach a total of 150, or challenge a partner.

Drawing together

Invite children to explain what they have discovered. Talk about work that shows an organized approach to finding a range of numbers, and work that shows clearly how answers were made.

Challenge the children to explain how certain numbers could be made:

How would you make 18 using 3 darts? Using 2 darts?
How would you make 36 using 6 darts? 24 using 3 darts? 24 using 4 darts? ...

Dartboard digits

Name -------------------------------

Umit throws four darts at the dartboard.

He always hits the target.

Find 13 different scores that he could make.

Set out your work clearly.

To score:

Add together the digits scored by each dart.

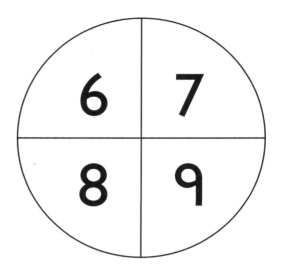

School on Planet Zoot

Teaching objectives
♦ solving multiplication and division problems
♦ looking for patterns
♦ making generalizations

Resources
♦ PCM 21
♦ 2p and 5p coins (real or plastic)
♦ paper

Formative assessment
Can the children explain the relationship between multiplication and division?

Children on Planet Zoot get paid by their teachers. There are only two types of coin: 5 zoo and 6 zoo. Work out how the teacher paid each child.

Getting started

Give each child a 2p coin and a 5p coin. Tell them that they have to work out which totals between 20p and 50p they can make using multiples of these coins.

Can you make 20p/21p/33p, …? How?

▶ **Key teaching point:** When you add odd numbers and even numbers, you can produce a range of numbers.

Independent task

Give the children a copy of PCM 21 and explain that the 5 zoo coins and 6 zoo coins are the only money that they can use to make the totals. Ask the children to predict what totals will be impossible to make and write these on the board. Tell the children to record how they made the total for each child on the PCM. They should also write an explanation on paper of any useful patterns or methods they found.

Developing the problem

- Look at the predictions for impossible numbers. Invite children to explain how they were able to solve some of these problems. Make a display of written explanations about useful patterns and methods discovered by the children.

- Show the children how to use multiples of 5 and 6 arranged in columns to help with this task, for example:
- Their next task is to investigate how they could make the totals between 260 and 272.

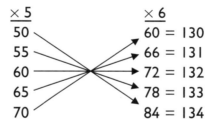

$$\begin{array}{ll}
\times 5 & \times 6 \\
50 & 60 = 130 \\
55 & 66 = 131 \\
60 & 72 = 132 \\
65 & 78 = 133 \\
70 & 84 = 134
\end{array}$$

FOLLOW-UP

- Use a 6 zoo coin and a 7 zoo coin. Can you still make the same totals?

- Investigate the totals that you can make by doubling and halving your solutions.

Drawing together

Invite children to explain what they have found. Compare interesting and shortcut methods that they have used.

School on Planet Zoot

Name --

You need: 2p and 5p coins, paper

Children on Planet Zoot get paid by their teachers.

There are only two types of coin: 5 zoo and 6 zoo.

Work out how the teacher paid each child.

Write about any patterns or methods you find.

The decimal swamp thing

Teaching objectives
◆ adding decimal fractions
◆ adding strings of decimal numbers
◆ developing systems for recording

Resources
◆ PCM 22
◆ counters (optional)
◆ paper (optional)

Formative assessment
Can the children add a series of simple decimal fractions?

Move through the decimal swamp by stepping on the stones. Add up the numbers on the stones that you step on. The swamp thing will get you if your total ends in ·5 or ·8.

Getting started

Give the children a copy of PCM 22 and work through a short journey through the swamp with them. Encourage the children to keep a running record of the total by drawing the jumps on a number line on the PCM.

Start at 0 and jump to the 0·3 stone and then to the 0·4 stone. What is our total now? Now jump to the 0·3 stone. What must our total be now? Now jump to the 0·8 stone. What is our new total? Oh no, the swamp thing has got us!

Tell the children to find ways of reaching the finish without being eaten.

Key teaching point: The addition of decimal fractions is similar to the addition of tens and units.

Independent task

Tell the children to use PCM 22 to discover ten different routes across the swamp without being eaten by the swamp thing. Tell them to each record route and final total either on a number line or on paper. They can use the back of the PCM for further working.

Developing the problem

● Invite children to describe one of their routes. Encourage the other children to follow this route, keeping a running total to check that the final total is correct.

● Show the children how to plot out their moves in advance, and to look for quick ways of adding strings of decimal numbers:

$0 + 0·3 + \widehat{0·4} + 0·3 + \widehat{1·1} + \widehat{0·9} + 0·3 + 0·2 + 0·5 + \widehat{0·6}$ …

Look for ways of making 1 first. Then you can decide whether to finish there or whether you need another stone first to avoid the swamp thing.

● Their next task is to arrange their final totals in order of size.

| FOLLOW-UP |

● Find the biggest and smallest totals that let you cross the swamp safely.

● Find five routes that allow the swamp thing to get you.

Drawing together

Invite children to explain their findings. Look at quick ways of adding decimals. Tell the children to play 'Swamp thing' with a partner. Pairs use one counter and one copy of PCM 22. They take it in turns to move the counter to an adjacent stone, each keeping a running record of their score. The aim is to make the running total end in ·5 or ·8. The player who makes this total is safe; their partner is eaten by the swamp thing! When someone is eaten, start again.

The decimal swamp thing

Name --

Move through the decimal swamp by stepping on the stones.

Add up the numbers on the stones that you step on.

The swamp thing will get you if your total ends in ·5 or ·8.

Record your moves on a number line.

0   1   2

Dice bingo

Teaching objectives
◆ interpreting data using graphs and
  diagrams
◆ exploring probability
◆ making statements based on findings

Resources
◆ PCM 23
◆ paper
◆ two dice of different sizes

Formative assessment
Can the children use frequency charts to
interpret data?

*Anil is trying to choose six lucky numbers for his
dice bingo grid. Explain how these diagrams
could help him.*

Getting started

Tell the children they are going to play a game of 'Dice bingo'. They need to draw a
grid with spaces for six numbers. Tell them you will roll two dice and call out the
numbers. They will then have to find the product of these numbers, for example, for
the dice numbers *6* and *2*: *6 × 2 = 12*. Ask the children to calculate the smallest
and largest numbers that can be made in this way and tell them to select six
numbers within this range and to write them on their grid. Roll the dice and call
out the numbers to be multiplied. The game finishes when a player has crossed off
all the numbers on their grid.

Key teaching point: Some numbers in the 1 to 36 range are impossible to make.

Independent task

Give the children a copy of PCM 23 and explain that they should complete Anil's
diagrams. Tell them to use these diagrams to work out which totals are impossible
and which might have more chances of being made. Tell them to use the completed
diagrams to help them write a list of suitable numbers for the 'Dice bingo' game.

Developing the problem

● Invite children to explain how the diagrams can be used to find out information
  about the numbers in the 'Dice bingo' game.
  *Why does Anil call some numbers 'lucky'? Which diagram shows the lucky
  numbers most clearly? Which diagram would you use to help you write some
  hints about choosing lucky numbers for the 'Dice bingo' game? What could you
  use to show the impossible numbers most clearly? (Mark off the numbers on a
  1–100 grid)*

● Their next task is to design a test to find out if the lucky numbers do occur more
  often in the game.

FOLLOW-UP

● Use diagrams to help you choose lucky numbers for a 'Multiplication bingo'
  game using two dice numbered 3 to 8.

● Use diagrams to help you choose lucky numbers for an 'Addition bingo' game
  using two dice numbered 1 to 6.

Drawing together

Draw grids with different selections of six numbers:
Let's make a grid of numbers with no chance of winning.
Can we make a grid of numbers that are certain to win?

Play 'Dice bingo' and cross off the numbers on these different grids to test whether
the children's predictions are correct.

Dice bingo

Name --

You need: paper

Anil is trying to choose six lucky numbers for his dice bingo grid.

Explain how the diagrams below could help him.

Anil's dice bingo grid

2	3	7	24		

Anil's method of working out totals

large dice

small dice

X	1	2	3	4	5	6
1	1	2	3	4	5	6
2	2	4	6			
3	3	6				
4	4	8				
5						
6						

Anil's frequency chart

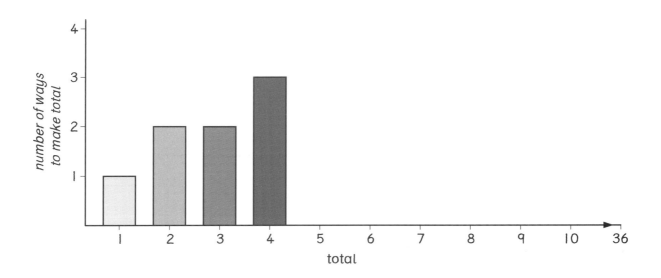

How to play dice bingo

Draw a dice bingo grid with six spaces.
Write down six different numbers on the grid.
Roll two dice and multiply the numbers.
If this number is on your grid, you can cross it off.
The game ends when you have crossed off all six numbers.

Naughty elephants

Teaching objectives
◆ using eight points of compass direction
◆ working systematically
◆ obtaining information

Resources
◆ PCM 24

Formative assessment
Can the children use their understanding
of the compass points to solve a problem?

▌ *Use the compass grid to solve the hidden messages.*

Getting started

Give the children a copy of PCM 24 and tell them to look at the title. Tell them to use the compass grid to work out what naughty elephants do (squirt water). Explain how the saying 'Naughty Elephants Squirt Water' can be used to remember the order of the compass points. Tell the children to write the name of the school using the compass code.

▶ **Key teaching point:** A point halfway between two compass points is described as north-east, north-west, south-east or south-west.

Independent task

Tell the children to use the compass grid to work out the coded message. Tell them to set their work out clearly to show how they turned each part of the code into a letter. Point out that some parts of the code leave out the number so the children have to choose the most appropriate letter. They must decide whether SW3 is letter X, Y or Z.

Developing the problem

● Write out the message a letter at a time by asking individual children to decode each letter. Look at examples of children's work that show a systematic approach which can be checked easily. Show the children how to make decoding easier by looking for letters that occur regularly, such as the vowels.

● Display the coded word *NE1 N1 S2 N1 S2 N1 (banana)*.
  Which letter would you decode first?
  If we work out that N1 stands for letter a, we've worked out half of the word already.
  Can you guess the word? What letter should we work out next? Can you guess now?

● Their next task is to work with a partner to write a coded message using the compass grid.

| FOLLOW-UP |

● Design your own version of the compass grid by moving the letters to different spaces. Write a coded message for a partner to solve.

● Write a coded elephant joke book.

Drawing together

Invite children to show their work and explain how they solved coded messages. Remind them of the importance of well organized work that records the code alongside the letter it represents. Explain how organized recording allows you to check your work.

Play 'Compass points'. The teacher labels one part of the room north and asks the class to move or point south, south-west, ….

Naughty elephants

Use the compass grid to solve the hidden messages.

Naughty elephants

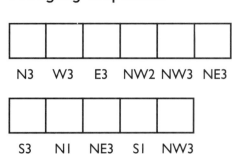

N3	W3	E3	NW2	NW3	NE3

S3	NI	NE3	SI	NW3

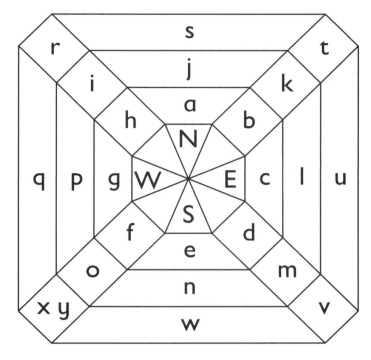

NWI SW2 S3   SEI SW☐   SI E2 SI W2 NWI NI S2 NE3 N3

_____

NW☐ NW2 SEI SI   NW☐ S☐   NEI SW2 S3 E2 N3

_____

SW2 SWI   E☐ E3 N3 NE3 NI NW3 SEI ?

_____

NE3 NWI SI SW3   W2 NI NW2 S2 NE3

_____

NE3 NWI SI SE☐ N3 SI E2 SE3 SI N3

_____

SW3 SI E☐ E☐ SW2 S3 .

_____

Halfway on the landing zone

Teaching objectives
◆ finding numbers between two numbers
◆ selecting maths
◆ presenting results

Resources
◆ PCM 25
◆ counters (two per child)
◆ demonstration 0–100 number line
◆ number line (one per pair)
◆ paper

Formative assessment
Can the children select the maths needed to work out which number lies exactly halfway between two other numbers?

Toss two counters onto the landing zone. Use the digits the counters land on to make a 2-digit number. Toss the counters again to make a second 2-digit number. Find the number that is halfway between your two numbers.

Find at least 12 different halfway numbers in this way.

Getting started

Circle two even numbers on a large number line, for example, *2 and 12*. Ask the children to work out the number that is exactly halfway between those two numbers. Tell the children to find the halfway number between other pairs of even numbers, for example, *2 and 14, 6 and 18, 10 and 20, 18 and 26, ...*

Key teaching point: The number that is halfway between two even numbers is always a whole number.

Independent task

Give the children a copy of PCM 25 and two counters. Demonstrate how to toss the counters to make 2-digit numbers. Explain that either number can be used as the tens or ones digit. For example, *4 and 6* could be written as *64* or *46*.

Tell the children to record their work neatly on paper, and to write an explanation of 'How to find the halfway number'.

Developing the problem

● Ask children to read out their explanations. They can read out two of their numbers and challenge the class to work out the halfway number.

● Remind the children how to find the difference between two numbers by subtracting the smaller from the larger. Explain that you can add half of the difference to the smaller number to find the halfway number:

The difference between 12 and 20 is 8. Half of 8 is 4. 12 + 4 = 16. 16 is halfway between 12 and 20.

FOLLOW-UP

● Toss three counters to make pairs of 3-digit numbers.

● Find the halfway number using pairs of odd numbers. What do you notice?

Drawing together

Using the demonstration number line, ask children to find the number that is halfway between pairs of odd numbers, for example, *1 and 9, 11 and 21.*

Explain that the number halfway between pairs of odd numbers is always a whole number.

Invite the children to show how they would find the number that is halfway between an even number and an odd number.

Halfway on the landing zone

Name --------------------------------

You need: two counters, a number line, paper

Toss two counters onto the landing zone.
Use the digits the counters land on to make a 2-digit number.
Toss the counters again to make a second 2-digit number.
Find the number that is halfway between your two numbers.

Find at least 12 different halfway numbers in this way.
Set out your work clearly.

If the counter misses the landing zone, toss it again.

If the counter is on a line between two or more digits, choose any one of those digits.

Landing zone

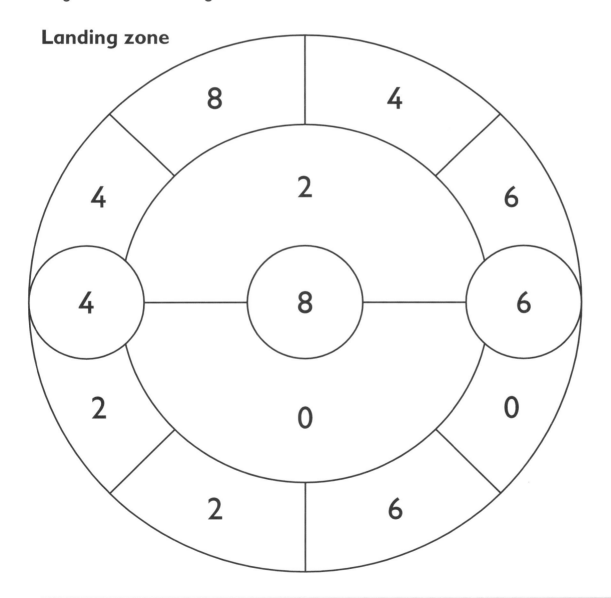

A smashing time

Teaching objectives
◆ using mental addition and subtraction
◆ using trial and improvement
◆ keeping a record of solutions tried

Resources
◆ PCM 26
◆ paper

Formative assessment
Can the children develop an organized approach to their search for solutions?

Nadia carries a pile of 100 plates across the restaurant. She drops the numbers of plates shown on the banana skins. She picks up the numbers of plates shown on the tables. Find the largest and smallest numbers of plates she can bring to the kitchen.

Getting started

Give the children a copy of PCM 26 and explain that you can only visit a square once on any journey. Follow a route through the restaurant by keeping a running record of Nadia's total. Challenge them to follow your route:

She started off with 100 and now she's got 110. Where is she? Whoops, that's 107. Where is she now? She's now got 114, ...

Invite children to take over the description of the route.

Key teaching point: Many additions and subtractions can be worked out in your head.

Independent task

Tell the children to try and find the largest and smallest numbers of plates Nadia can bring to the kitchen. They should keep a record on paper of the journeys they made to produce the different totals.

Developing the problem

● Ask children to show their work, and to explain how they calculated and kept track of the totals. Show examples of recorded routes that did not produce the largest or smallest number of plates. Explain how keeping a record of all the routes can help you narrow down the search, and can prevent you trying the same routes twice. Show the children how to keep a record of routes and running totals:

Route 1		Route 2	
Start	100	Start	100
+10	110	+15	115
+20	130	–8	107, ...

● Their next task is to work with a partner to find 12 different totals.

FOLLOW-UP

● Find out what different totals could be made if Nadia started off with 27 plates.

● Make up your own version of the game using different numbers.

Drawing together

Display a large copy of the game board from PCM 26 and invite children to come and trace one of their routes slowly using a finger and giving the instructions:

100 + 15 + 20 + 4, ...

Challenge the rest of the class to work out the final total.

A smashing time

Name --

You need: paper

Nadia carries a pile of 100 plates across the restaurant.
She drops the numbers of plates shown on the banana skins.
She picks up the numbers of plates shown on the tables.
Find the largest and smallest numbers of plates she can bring to
the kitchen.

Record your work clearly on paper.

Remember

Nadia can visit each square once only on each journey.

Moves can be made only in a vertical or horizontal direction.

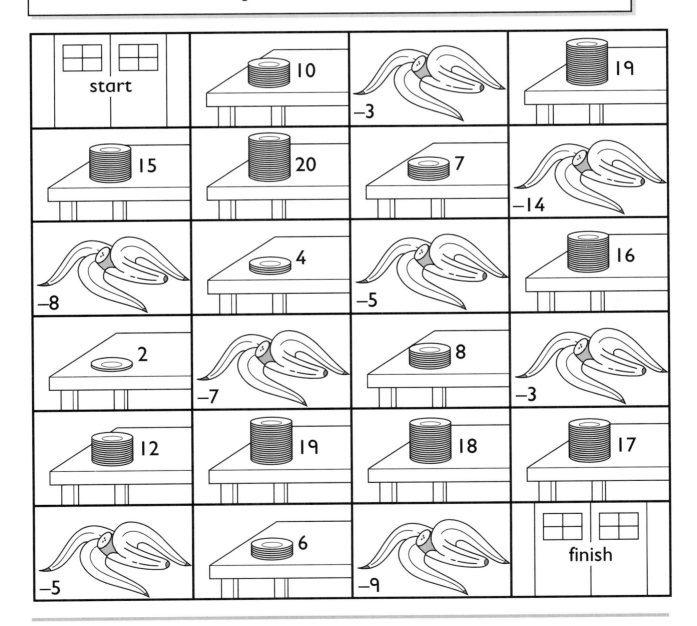

Card capers

Teaching objectives
◆ using standard written methods of
   addition and subtraction
◆ looking for a range of solutions
◆ checking results

Resources
◆ PCM 27
◆ scissors

Formative assessment
Can the children use addition and
subtraction as inverse operations to check
answers?

*Make 16 different numbers using five of the
digit cards.*

Getting started

Give the children a copy of PCM 27 and explain how the digit cards
should be cut out and placed on the algorithm outline to produce different answers.
Tell them to work out how the children in the picture made their answers. Show the
children how to create different numbers by changing the order of the cards.

▶ **Key teaching point:** The position of a digit card determines its place value.

Independent task

Tell the children to make 16 different numbers, keeping a record of how they made
each one. Tell them that they should check each answer to make sure that their work
is accurate. Ask them to write a short explanation of their method for checking.

Developing the problem

● The children make a display of their answers. Ask other children to guess whether
  the number was made through addition or subtraction. Ask the child what method
  they used to make their number. Invite suggestions as to how the method can be
  checked.

  *The calculation is 564 – 46 = 518. I'm going to check that by adding
  518 + 46. If the answer is 564 then I know that the calculation is correct.*

  *You can use addtion to check subtraction. Add the answer to the number you took
  away. If the calculation is correct, this should equal, the number you started with.*

● Their next task is to work with a partner to work out the largest and smallest
  numbers that can be made using addition and subtraction.

FOLLOW-UP

● Challenge a partner to a game of 'Find my sum'. Work out a sum using the digit
  cards without your partner seeing. Tell them the answer and ask them to work
  out how you made it.

● Make 16 different numbers again, using all six digit cards. Start with a
  4-digit number and then add or subtract a 2-digit number.

Drawing together

Display some incorrect calculations similar to the ones tackled in the problem:

664 + 45 = 619   466 + 55 = 411   644 – 55 = 699   464 – 55 = 411

*Check these calculations. Can anyone see any problems? How did you check this
one? Did anyone use a different method? What is wrong? Can you see the mistake?*

Card capers

Name --------------------------------

You need: scissors

Make 16 different numbers using five of the digit cards below.

Record your work clearly.

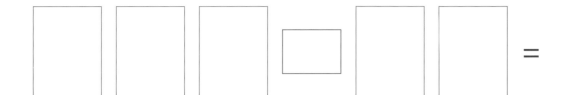

=

I made 611 and 411 using subtraction.

I made 699. I think that's the biggest number you can make.

Numeracy Focus 4: Problem of the Week

Anyone for tennis?

Teaching objectives
◆ drawing lines to an accuracy of 5 mm
◆ following instructions
◆ using diagrams

Resources
◆ PCM 28
◆ paper
◆ rulers and paper-clips

Formative assessment
Can the children find all the information needed from a set of plans?

▌ *Draw an accurate plan for a tennis court.*

Getting started

Give the children a copy of PCM 28 and a sheet of plain paper.
Show them how to use the cross on the PCM as a guideline for drawing accurate right angles. Tell them to draw a series of rectangles with the guideline:

Draw a set of rectangles with an area of 24 cm². Each should have a different perimeter.

Work out one or two examples on the board with them first.

Key teaching point: Shapes with different perimeters can have the same area.

Independent task

Give the children a copy of PCM 28 and explain that they have to draw an accurate plan of a tennis court. Tell them to draw their plan on plain paper and remind them how to use the cross on the PCM as a guideline.

Developing the problem

● Look at the plans drawn by some of the children and invite volunteers to check some of the lengths on the plans. Ask children to explain how they worked out the lengths of those lines not labelled on the PCM.

   How many rectangles can you see on the plan of the tennis court?
   What is the perimeter/area of this shape?

● Their next task is to calculate areas and perimeters of the different parts of their plan.

FOLLOW-UP

● Draw an enlarged copy of the tennis court on a large sheet of paper, or in the playground using chalk.

● Draw plans for other sports pitches.

Drawing together

Display the finished plans and invite children to explain how they made sure that their drawings were accurate. Ask children to indicate pairs of lines of equal length.

Tell the children to count the number of quadrilaterals inside the plan. Ask them to explain how they calculated the area and perimeter of some of these quadrilaterals within the plan. Ask them to check the measurements on a partner's plan.

Anyone for tennis?

Name --

You need: paper, a ruler, paper-clips

Draw an accurate plan for a tennis court.

Remember

Use the drawing to find the length of each line.

Use the cross below as a guideline to help you draw accurate right angles.

Guideline for drawing right angles

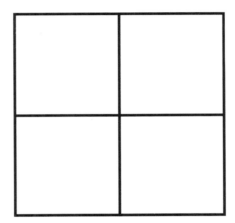 

Drawing of tennis court

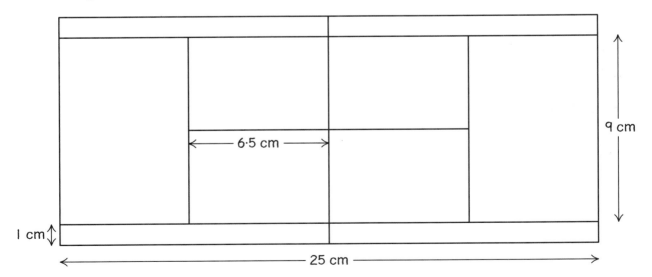

6·5 cm

9 cm

1 cm

25 cm

The Great Escape goats

Teaching objectives
◆ using angle and rotation
◆ giving accurate instructions
◆ refining a problem

Resources
◆ PCM 29
◆ paper

Formative assessment
Can the children use appropriate language associated with angle and rotation?

Three little goats have escaped from the farm. Record their escape routes.

Getting started

Give the children a copy of PCM 29 and read through the description of nanny's escape route. Tell the children to work out which of the routes on the map shows nanny's escape.

How do we know in which direction she turned? How do we know how far she turned in that direction? What words can you use to give information about a turn?

Key teaching point: Turns can be measured and described using angle and the word 'clockwise' or 'anticlockwise'.

Independent task

Tell the children to label nanny's escape route on the map. Ask them to write descriptions of the routes taken by Gruff and Billy on a sheet of paper.

Developing the problem

● Invite children to read out their written descriptions of the escape routes. Tell the other children to follow these descriptions by tracing their finger along the routes on their maps.

Could you use different words in place of 'turn right'?
Which way is anticlockwise? How do you know that is 45°/90°?

● Their next task is to invent the name for a fourth goat and describe the remaining escape route on the map.

FOLLOW-UP

A second copy of PCM 29 may be needed for each of these follow-up activities.

● Work out an escape route using only 30° and 60° turns.

● Write out a description of a new escape route and challenge a partner to draw it on the map.

Drawing together

● Make a display of the different escape-route maps and descriptions.

● Play a game of 'Escape goat'. Children are invited to walk to the door in short stages. Other children describe each stage of their movement.

Which way did she turn? How many degrees was that turn? How could we ask her to turn and face in the opposite direction? Is a right turn the same as a clockwise turn?

The Great Escape goats

Name --

You need: paper

Three little goats have escaped from the farm.

Record their escape routes.

Billy's Escape

I turned 45° anticlockwise at the gate and ran off.

My Escape by nanny

I ran straight out of the gate.
I turned 45° clockwise and kept running.
I turned 45° anticlockwise and ran on.
My next turn was a right angle clockwise.
After running on for a while I turned 90° left.
Then I ran straight into the woods.

The Tale of Gruff

I ran straight out of the gate and then did a 90° turn clockwise.

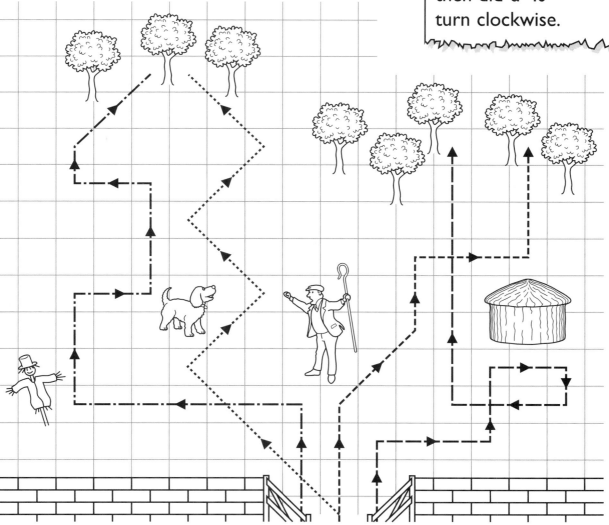

Climbing stairs

Teaching objectives
◆ breaking down a problem
◆ checking results
◆ obtaining information

Resources
◆ PCM 30
◆ calculator

Formative assessment
Can the children break down a problem
and obtain the information needed to
solve it?

*Freya works out the height of the stairs from
the playground to her classroom.
She adds up all the times she climbs these
stairs in a year and gets a total height taller
than Mount Everest.
Her brother Joey says that she has got her sums wrong.
Work out who is correct.*

Getting started

Give the children a copy of PCM 30 and explain the problem that Freya is
attempting to solve. Explain that her brother has found some errors in her
calculations but hasn't marked them. Ask the children to check whether Freya has
calculated the total height of the stairs correctly.

Key teaching point: Setting out work in clearly organized stages allows you to check
the work and spot errors more easily.

Independent task

Ask the children to go through Freya's calculations, checking for errors and working
out the true height climbed in a year. Tell them to ring the errors and set out their
own calculations in a similar way to Freya's.

Developing the problem

● Invite children to point out some of Freya's mistakes. Explain that Freya seems to
know what she is trying to do but that she has made some errors:

the total height of the staircase is wrong;

she says she goes up the stairs three times each day but has only multiplied by 2,

she doesn't go to school 365 days each year (39 weeks × 5 days is closer to the
number of school days);

she has set out her columns incorrectly when working out 365 days multiplied by
the total height climbed each day;

she has mixed up cm and m when recording the height of Mount Everest.

● Their next task is to use Freya's methods to work out an estimate of the height she
climbs each year.

FOLLOW-UP

● Work out an estimate of the height you climb each year using stairs at
school/home.

● Work out how many hours you spend sitting at your desk each year.

Drawing together

Compare the calculation made by the children with those made by Freya. Ask
children to show how they worked out different parts of the problem. Ask them to
explain the workings of any written calculations they used.

Climbing stairs

Name --

Freya works out the height of the stairs from the playground to her classroom.

She adds up all the times she climbs these stairs in a year and gets a total height taller than Mount Everest.

Her brother Joey says that she has got her sums wrong.

Work out who is correct. Set out your work clearly.

How I climbed Mount Everest last year by Freya aged 6.

The stairs are 18 cm tall.
There are 20 stairs.

10×18 cm $= 180$ cm

10×18 cm $= 180$ cm

```
    180
 +  180
 _____
    810 cm
    6
```

I go up the stairs three times each day.

2×180

$\times$	100	80
2	200	160

$200 + 160 = 360$ cm

So I climb 360 cm each day.

I go to school 365 days each year.
So I climb 360 cm $\times$ 365 days.

360 cm $\times$ 100 days =   36 000 cm

360 cm $\times$ 100 days =   36 000 cm

360 cm $\times$ 100 days =   36 000 cm

360 cm $\times$ 50 days =   18 000 cm

360 cm $\times$ 10 days =   3 600 cm

360 cm $\times$ 5 days =   1 800 cm

                      147 600 cm

                      3

There are 100 cm in 1 metre so 147 000 ÷ 100 = 1470 metres.

So every year I climb 1470 metres up the stairs.

Mount Everest is 8848 cm tall so I climb higher than that every year.

Now how did you do that?

Teaching objectives
◆ using operations to solve puzzles
◆ looking for a range of solutions
◆ working systematically

Resources
◆ PCM 31

Formative assessment
Can the children organize their approach in a systematic way?

Make 21 different numbers using the digits 3, 4 and 5. You can add, subtract, multiply or divide the digits.

Getting started

Tell the children they are going to calculate different numbers using just three digits. Display the digits *1*, *2* and *3*. Show the children that the digits can be added to make 6. Rearrange the digits so they read *2 + 3 + 1* and ask if the total is different. Repeat for *3 + 1 + 2*.

Write down the calculation *23 + 1 = 24*. Tell the children to work out how to make *15 (12 + 3)* and *33 (32 + 1)*. Tell them to find other numbers using addition, subtraction, multiplication and division.

Key teaching point: Some operations can be done in any order to produce the same result. For example, *32 + 1 = 31 + 2, 3 × 2 × 1 = 2 × 3 × 1*, ...

Independent task

Give the children a copy of PCM 31 and tell them to use the three digits to make 21 different numbers. Tell them to record how they made each number. Ask them to predict the highest and lowest numbers that will be possible, and record these predictions.

Developing the problem

● Make a display of the numbers made by the children. Collect them by asking for categories of calculation, such as those using addtion only. Ask children to explain their methods.

● Show the children how to organize their approach by looking for all the combinations of the digits so that they find the widest possible range of solutions.

3 + 4 + 5 = 12. Do we need to try 5 + 4 + 3? Why?

Next we can try 34 + 5, 43 + 5 and 53 + 4. Why don't we need to try 5 + 34 or 35 + 4? Have we found all of the answers using addition?

● Invite children to add solutions to the display of numbers organized in categories, such as 'Solutions using division. Encourage the children to look for new solutions that could produce a different answer.

● Display the calculations *3 + 4 × 5 = 35* and *3 + 4 × 5 = 23*. Ask the children to consider which answer could be correct. Their next task is to find other sums that can provide more than one answer.

FOLLOW-UP

● Write some hints for someone investigating problems like the one on the PCM.

● Find 20 numbers using the digits 7, 8 and 9.

Drawing together

Play 'How did you do that?'. Children take it in turns to call out a number from the display. The teacher asks, 'How did you do that?' and other children explain.

Now how did you do that?

Make 21 different numbers using the digits 3, 4 and 5.

You can add, subtract, multiply or divide the digits.

Set out your work clearly.

thirty-four take away five…

three take away fifty-four…

fifty-three add four…

I can make 70 and 49…

The top of the tower

Teaching objectives
- multiplying 2- and 3-digit numbers
- selecting when to use written or mental methods
- checking results

Resources
- PCM 32
- paper

Formative assessment
Can the children apply their understanding of multiplication and division?

Use your multiplication and division skills to find 17 different numbers at the top of the tower.

Getting started

Give the children a copy of PCM 32 and explain how the tower works. Tell the children to find different numbers for the top of the tower by using 5 from the left pile and any of the numbers in the right pile. Then show the children how to check their answers using division.

Key teaching point: Division can be used to check multiplication and vice versa.

Independent task

Tell the children to shade in the 5 brick in the left pile as this can no longer be used. They can now investigate how to make 17 different numbers at the top of the tower. Tell them to record their calculations and how they checked them on paper.

Developing the problem

- Invite children to explain when they decided to use written rather than mental calculations. Look at the range of written methods they used to calculate and check solutions. Ask them when it might not be necessary to write down calculations:

  If you worked out $2 \times 2 = 4$ in your head, do you need to write that down and $4 \div 2 = 2$?

- Discuss with the children how all the numbers are even numbers. Invite them to suggest how to change numbers in the left and right piles to make odd number answers. Encourage them to investigate with small numbers to make the calculations easier.

FOLLOW-UP

- Make a tower using any of the bricks. Copy out your tower again, but this time write in only the number at the top of the tower. Give this copy to a friend and ask them to work out how you made the number.

- Make a tower problem using three single-digit bricks at the bottom. How many different numbers can you make using the same three numbers?

Drawing together

Invite children to show their work and explain what they have discovered. Show an empty tower of three bricks and write a number at the top. Ask them to suggest numbers that will produce that number.

If the top number is 36, which multiplication and division facts might help us work out the other numbers? How can we check that's correct?

The top of the tower

Name ---------------------------------------

You need: paper

Use your multiplication and division skills to find 17 different numbers at the top of the tower.

Set out your work clearly on paper.

Rules

❶ Choose one brick from each pile to put in the spaces at the bottom of the tower.

❷ Multiply the number on each brick by 2. Write the answers in the bricks above them.

❸ Multiply the numbers on the middle row together to find the number on the top brick.

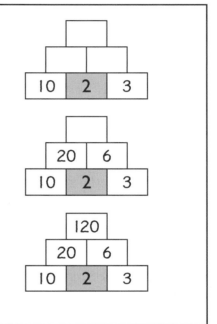

tower

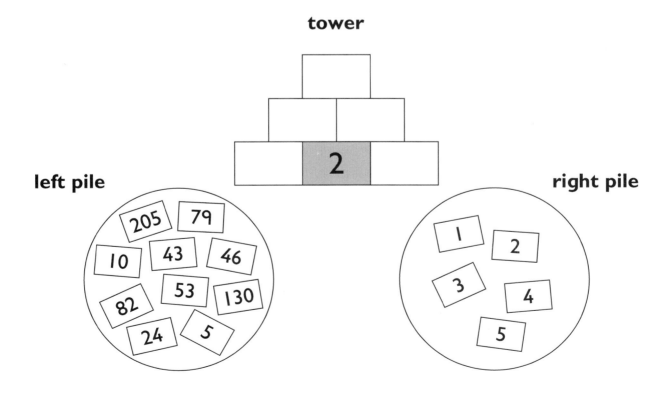

left pile   **right pile**

Diary of a cycling holiday

Make a diary showing how the children share the cost of their holiday.

Teaching objectives
- solving division problems
- making decisions about remainders
- explaining reasoning

Resources
- PCM 33
- counters
- coins (real or plastic)
- paper

Formative assessment
Can the children explain their reasoning when dealing with remainders?

Getting started

Give the children a copy of PCM 33 and look at the diary page at the bottom. Ask them to work out how much each of the three children paid for the bicycle. Tell them to record their work on the diary page on the PCM, and to explain how they dealt with any remainders. Read the rules of the game.

Key teaching point: Decisions about remainders in division sums have to be based on the context of the question.

Independent task

Tell the children to play the game. Ask them to make a diary page on paper to record all the division problems they solve, and to explain how they dealt with any remainders.

Developing the problem

- Invite children to read through some of the problems they have solved. Look at different methods used to calculate the answers and draw attention to the relationship between multiplication and division:

We use multiples of 3 when solving these problems.

To share 465 cherries it helps to know that $3 \times 100 = 300$
$3 \times 50 = 150$
$3 \times 5 = 15$

Who can explain how this helps?

- Ask children to explain decisions they have made about dealing with remainders.
- Their next task is to work out in pairs what happens if the numbers to be shared are all doubled.

FOLLOW-UP

- Play the game again, using a bicycle with six children on it. What do you notice?
- Invent your own version of the game with different division problems to solve.

Drawing together

Make a display of some of the diary pages made by the children. Ask children to explain their reasoning when dealing with some of the problems:

When you shared out the number of pictures that could be taken with the camera, how many pictures were left over? What did you decide to do with it? Does it make sense not to take a picture that is left over?

If a bill can't be shared equally, is it all right not to pay the amount that remains? What should you do?

How do you share litres/kilograms?

Name --

You need: counters, a coin, paper

Make a diary showing how the children share the cost of their holiday.

Rules

Use a counter to represent the children on their bicycle.

Toss a coin.

Heads means move your counter 1 space. Tails means move 2 spaces. On each space your counter lands on, divide the amount by 3 and record it on paper.

Fill in a new diary page when you reach home and explain your work.

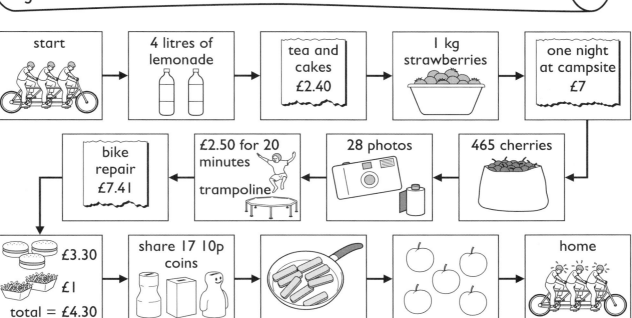

Diary page

My name is ———————————— .

I bought a 3-seater bicycle with my friends ——————— and ——————— .

We paid £15.20 for our bicycle. This is how we worked out our share of the cost:

Belal's birthday bash

Teaching objectives
- using the language of ratio and proportion
- deciding what information is needed
- selecting maths to use

Resources
- PCM 34

Formative assessment
Can the children use their understanding of ratio and proportion to solve a range of problems?

Help Belal to plan his birthday party by completing the shopping list.

Getting started

Give the children a copy of PCM 34 and ask them to look at the cheese and pineapple stick. Ask them to work out how many pieces of cheese and pineapple would be needed to make one stick each for 50 children. Repeat for the gherkin and onion stick.

Key teaching point: The term 'for every' can be used to describe the amount of each item required, for example, *we need 2 pieces of cheese for every piece of pineapple.*

Independent task

Tell the children to complete the shopping list, showing the number of each item to be bought. Tell them to record the calculations they use to work out the amounts needed.

Developing the problem

- Invite children to show their work and explain their methods. Look at the calculations recorded by the children.

- Show the children how drawing a picture of the problem can help to clarify the problem:

   The ice-cream floats are made in 500 ml glasses. I'm drawing a rough picture of a 500 ml glass and I'm going to draw lines to divide it up into 5 equal parts. Each part must hold 100 ml. The recipe says that 3 parts will be cola, that's 300 ml. 1 part is lemonade (100 ml) and 1 part ice-cream (100 ml). So we'll need to buy 50 × 100 ml of lemonade, which is 5000 ml, or 5 litres.

- Their next task is to work with a partner to check through their calculations and estimate what the shopping bill will cost.

FOLLOW-UP

- Design some meals on sticks. Use the words 'for every' in recipes for your meals.

- Find examples of recipes that use ratio or proportion.

Drawing together

Look at the calculations used to make the shopping lists. Ask the children a series of questions and use drawings to illustrate the answers:

Donna ate 4 cheese and pineapple sticks for every 1 that Ann ate. Anne ate 3, so how many did Donna eat?

Shiloh drank 3 ice-cream floats for every 1 that Megan had. If Megan had 4, how many did Shiloh drink?

Belal's birthday bash

Name ------------------------------------

Help Belal to plan his birthday party by completing the shopping list.

There will be 50 children at the party.

Belal wants there to be enough food and drink for everyone to have one of everything.

Recipes

Sticks

1 pineapple and 2 cheese

1 gherkin and 3 onions

Ice-cream floats

Each 500 ml glass needs:

3 parts cola (300 ml)

1 part lemonade (100 ml)

1 part ice-cream (100 ml)

Flap-jack biscuits

To make 10 biscuits you need:

100 g butter

100 g sugar

100 g syrup

300 g porridge oats

Shopping list

1 kg cheese

1 tin pineapple

_____ gherkins

_____ onions

_____ litres of cola

_____ litres of lemonade

_____ litres of ice-cream

_____ g of butter

_____ g of sugar

_____ g of syrup

_____ g of porridge oats

The sponsored swim

Teaching objectives
◆ interpreting information from a table
◆ using trial and improvement methods
◆ developing approaches to problem solving

Resources
◆ PCM 35

Formative assessment
Can the children develop and refine strategies using trial and improvement?

Kelly and Sammi have finished their sponsored swim.
Use the information on their sponsor forms to work out how many lengths of the pool each girl swam.

Getting started

Give the children a copy of PCM 35 and explain that the girls have completed their swim and collected the money that was promised by their sponsors. Explain that some people sponsored the girls so much per length whilst others paid a set amount for the whole swim. Ask the children to count up the money shown on the sponsor sheets and write in the grand totals.

Key teaching point: When interpreting data presented in tables and charts, care must be taken to read any written information with the data.

Independent task

Tell the children to use the information shown on the sponsor sheets to work out the number of lengths each girl swam. Tell them to record how they worked it out including any attempts that were incorrect but which helped them solve the problem.

Developing the problem

● Invite children to explain their approaches to the problem. Show the children how the problem can be simplified by subtracting the set amounts from the grand total collected. The remaining money must have come from the amounts per length.

● Show the children how trial and improvement can be used to work out the number of lengths:
Sammi raised £20.28, of which £9.00 was a set amount.
£20.28 – £9.00 = £11.28, which was paid per length.
If we guess she swam 10 lengths, 20p × 10 = £2.00, 15p × 10 = £1.50, ... We'd reach a total of £9.40 which is less than £11.28. So Sammi must have swum more than 10 lengths.

Their next task is to work out how much money each girl would have raised if she had swum just one more length.

FOLLOW-UP

● Draw new sponsor forms to show how far each girl would have to swim in order to raise twice as much money from the same sponsors.

● Draw up a sponsor form puzzle problem for a friend to solve.

Drawing together

Invite children to explain how they solved the problem. Look at the stages they used and draw attention to the numbers chosen to start a trial and improvement approach:

Why might it be easier to work out the totals for 10 lengths or 100 lengths? If you know the total for 10 lengths can you work out the total for 5 lengths or 20 lengths? How?

The sponsored swim

Name --------------------------------

Kelly and Sammi have finished their sponsored swim.

Use the information on their sponsor forms to work out how many lengths of the pool each girl swam.

FROGSPAWN COUNTY JUNIOR SCHOOL

• *Sponsored swim* •

Swimmer's name   Sammi

Lengths completed _____

Name	Amount per length	Set amount
M. Mows	20p	
D. Durck		£4. 00
B. Sympsin	15p	
L. Sympsin	10p	
Kenny	40p	
K. Urmit		£3.00
H. Oma	9p	
B. Utter		£2.00
	Grand total	_____

FROGSPAWN COUNTY JUNIOR SCHOOL

• *Sponsored swim* •

Swimmer's name   Kelly

Lengths completed _____

Name	Amount per length	Set amount
Dyna Mite	16p	
D. Ogg		£8.00
O. Meyomy	20p	
Doug Deep		£4.00
Tony Capp	8p	
Orson Kart	6p	
I. Mameanie	1p	
I. Munot		£7.00
	Grand total	_____

Class President

Every child in the class is to spend one hour as Class President. Draw a timetable showing when each person gets their turn.

Teaching objectives
◆ representing data in timetables
◆ using appropriate tables
◆ presenting results

Resources
◆ PCM 36
◆ list of children in the class
◆ paper
◆ list of teachers in the school (for Follow-up)

Formative assessment
Can the children organize and interpret data using timetables?

Getting started

Ask the children to list important times from the school day, for example, start of school, playtimes, lunch and so on. Show them how to draw a chart to help them work out the length of the school day:

School starts		Next o'clock time		Last o'clock time		School ends
9:20	40 min	10:00	5 hours	3:00	35 min	3:35

Total = 5 hours + 40 minutes + 35 minutes = 6 hours 15 minutes

Tell them to draw a similar chart to help them work out the length of their school day.

Key teaching point: Diagrams and tables can help to make a problem easier to solve.

Independent task

Give the children a copy of PCM 36 and ask for suggestions about what the role of Class President might be. Tell them to produce a timetable that shows clearly when each person in their class should have their turn. Tell them to make sure that each person has a fair turn.

Developing the problem

● Display the timetables around the class and ask the children to decide which ones are easiest to read. Invite children to explain which timetables they feel are clear.
What information does the timetable need to tell us? Is it easy to see your name? Can you see what time you start/finish? What day will you get your turn? Is it fair that some people are President only at lunchtime or at times when we aren't in school?

● Their next task is to work with a partner to find out how long each person is President during lesson time.
How many turns will everyone get in each term?

| FOLLOW-UP |

● Draw a timetable so each teacher in your school is King or Queen for a day.

● Draw a timetable so each of the children in your class is Prime Minister for one week.

Drawing together

Look at the display of the various timetables and ask the children to explain any improvements they would make to their own timetables. Ask the class to suggest any further improvements that might be necessary.

Class President

Name --------------------------------

You need: a list of children in your class, paper

Every child in the class is to spend one hour as Class President.

Draw a timetable showing when each person gets their turn.

It's not fair, we were all swimming when it was my turn.